GODS
HEROES
&MONSTERS

TIM'S ADVENTURES IN
THE WORLD OF GREEK MYTHOLOGY

Graphic design: Maria-Christina Katsichti
Proof reading – editing for the Greek texts: Despoina Papagiannopoulou
Picture editing: Marcos Kouklakis
Project Coordination of Translation from Greek & Editing:
COM N. Pratsinis- K. Zissimou General Partnership (www.pra-zis.gr)

POLARIS PUBLISHERS: BOOKS – MULTIMEDIA
Navarinou 17, 10681 Athens
Tel.: (+30) 2103836482, Fax (+30) 2103807608
www.polarisekdoseis.gr, info@polarisekdoseis.gr

ISBN: 978-960-6829-70-3

ASPASIA PROTOGEROU

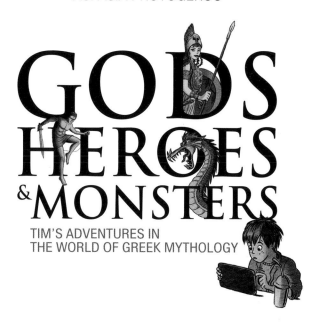

GODS HEROES & MONSTERS

TIM'S ADVENTURES IN
THE WORLD OF GREEK MYTHOLOGY

ILLUSTRATIONS ALECOS PAPADATOS
COLOUR ANNIE DI DONNA

POLARIS PUBLISHERS

CONTENTS

BY ZEUS!
MY SCREEN CAME TO LIFE!

I was bored. I was bored to tears. What was I doing in an archaeological museum?

When my parents announced, 'we are going on holiday to Greece', I thought, 'wow!' My mind flooded with beautiful images: the bright sun and the warm sand, turquoise waters, adventures, music, friends and fun...Well, none of these thoughts included a museum visit! An old building in central Athens full of - what else - boring old things, made hundreds of years before Christ stepped on earth! The place was stuffed with chunks of marble, broken ceramics and statues. Obscure scriptures as if written with a drunk bird's footprints. And faces too: loads of unfamiliar characters. A mishmash of gods (the ancient Greeks had many of those, you see) and heroes, warriors and half-gods, philosophers and rulers, ordinary people and mythical beasts. History and mythology all jumbled together!

Let me tell you one thing: thank goodness I took my tablet with me!

While my parents were wholeheartedly devoted to studying one of the innumerable exhibits, I sat in a corner, trying to pass unnoticeable. As still as a statue!

I was doing pretty well: my fingers were on fire, and I was about to achieve the highest score in my favourite game. Yes! I was this close to a level so high, it was believed to be a myth! When...

The screen of the tablet blacked out! Oh, come on! Not now! What is wrong with it? It was charged all right. Could it be that it died? I switched it off and on again, but nothing happened. Until all of a sudden, a strange bearded man appeared; he was grim, and he was wearing a white tunic, a chiton. He started talking to me in my own language. How bizarre!

'I can see you are defying both gods and humans, young mortal boy. Our glorious past leaves you unmoved. Not only do you not know or admire our glorious feats, but you also view us with scorn and indifference. You are boasting of your performance in a pointless game. All right then. I dare you mortal boy! Can you make it in a different kind of game? Do you have the guts to fight gods and beasts of supernatural powers? I swear to my divine beard, that when you get acquainted with the great protagonists of Greek mythology, and when you share some of their adventures, then our world will not seem that boring after all...'

The bearded man with the white chiton was fun! He had taken over my tablet however, and that was not fun at all. I guess I had to play the game anyway...

'You silly little mortal boy, that "funny bearded man" is the king of the gods of the ancient Greeks! I am Olympian Zeus, the father of all gods and mortals! I hold the power to gather clouds and bring about thunderstorms. I could make you disappear at once for such a great impiety! Lucky you, I am also Zeus Xenios, the patron of strangers. You see, for the Greeks, hospitality - xenia - was an honourable practice, and I - their supreme ruler - was entrusted with the task of guarding it. Every guest in my country is enjoying my absolute protection. Anyway, shall I presume you accept the challenge?'

Wait a minute! Was my tablet taken over by the spirit of a mytho-logical god, who could read my thoughts? A-MA-ZING!!! I have to admit: although I have played hundreds of interactive games, I wouldn't even dream of playing a game like this one! But what was I supposed to do? I knew almost nothing about Greek mythology...

'I will be your guide you mortal boy,' Zeus responded to my thoughts immediately. 'Mind you, I am well-known for my prudence. You will be challenged with trials that match your very own powers. But first, you must learn a few things about us, the gods of ancient Greece.'

All at once, an ancient Greek city popped up on my screen, just be-hind the god: with its brick-houses and its marble-columned temples, its assembly, its sculptures and its dwellers. Just like the bearded god, these people were wearing that very same short cloak called chlamys; there were merchants selling their goods, a craftsman making clay-pots, a blacksmith striking a sword on his anvil, a musician singing and playing the lyre, a man drawing shapes on the ground while teaching geometry to his pupils, teenage athletes training for wrestling, and fi-nally, an artist sculpting fine white marble into a stunning female nude - the young goddess of beauty and love, beyond any doubt.

'You see, we gods of the ancient Greeks are not distant and mysteri-ous like the gods of other cultures. We have human qualities, not only in form but also in spirit. We are of course immortal, looking immaculate and timeless, with perfect physical harmony and sturdiness, and with su-pernatural powers of all sorts and kinds. But at the same time, just like humans, we differ in character and complexion, preferences and dislikes, passions and flaws. Our life interweaves with the life of humans. We con-trol them and they control us. Mortals intervene in our adventures and we intervene in theirs. For example, just as it happens in human politics, I too had to struggle in order to establish full control in the world of gods. You see, I was not the first of the gods. The creation of the world took place before our divine existence. They conceived the beginning as nothing but void space, a prevailing Chaos. They then visualised the emergence of mother earth, Gaia, and that of Eros who, contrary to what you might think, acted more like a cosmic force; the glue that held all elements together. It is from the union of these two gods that Uranus, the god of the sky, was born and wept rain on Gaia, who then started producing life. Their children included, among others, the Titans - Cronus and Oceanus for example - the Giants, the Cyclops and the Nymphs.

Before land and the seas had acquired their familiar features, massive earthquakes and immense changes took place in earth's atmosphere and crust. God Uranus, who was causing extreme weather conditions, was fighting against his earthy children, until one of them, Cronus, prevailed in the end. He, the god of chronos (time), and his wife Rhea (the one who flows), regulated the cycles of seasons and established the flow of natural life.

It was now my turn to claim supreme authority; to become the ruler of heaven and earth. I defeated my father, who represented an older generation, and I crashed the Titans, whose powers disturbed the natural order. I marked the dawn of a new era for gods and humans; an era that would see the reign of the mind. Not only am I the supreme god of ancient Greece, but also the protector and the guardian of the natural and moral order in the universe. I stand for spiritual growth and the human thirst for progress, which has inspired them for such extraordinary accomplishments...One moment. What are you doing human? Are you yawning while Zeus is talking to you? How disgraceful! Beware you poor little boy, or I swear to god - that is me - this is not going to end very well!'

Oh no! I had almost forgotten. The bearded king could actually see me. I choked and wondered when the game would start.

'All right then. If you think that all these struggles to succeed was a piece of cake then it's about time you get your feet wet!'

Next thing I knew the peaceful ancient city disappeared, and my screen flooded with scenes of utter disaster. All you could see was mud, blood-soaked soil and enormous black mountains. Flashes of lightning were slashing the horizon in the background of a blood red sky. Suddenly, the tablet vibrated forcibly, and the ground pictured on the screen split open! A huge monster emerged from inside, one that I had never seen before, not even in a science fiction movie: he out-topped all the mountains. From his shoulders grew one hundred dragon heads. He had the torso of a man, but he had gigantic wings and enormous snake coils in place of legs. His one hundred heads bore fire-flashing eyes and black mouths with forked tongues. His shrill screams were giving me the goose bumps!

'Let me introduce you to Typhon, you mortal boy. He is the last Titan that still fights me, and the only enemy from the chaotic old days left to defeat. I will now need your help! You must give me my weapon. I have to fight him! Quick! What are you waiting for?' Zeus flew away just seconds before Typhon's enormous hands rushed to crash him.

What was this about? How was I supposed to help Zeus? How would I know where his weapon is?

'Oh, for the love of my name! Hurry up boy! I will try to hold him off by climbing Mount Olympus, the highest mountain in Greece.'

In a single bound, Zeus flew on the peak of a huge mountain. But Typhon was enormous, and this mountain seemed like a normal hill next to him. The monster pulled out smaller mountains, and started hurling them at Zeus. In the meantime, thousands of flames shooting from his eyes were already targeting the god.

'Where is your mastery boy? Use your mind, and pass me my weapon NOW!'

I was beating my brains out. No doubt his weapon was right in front

of me. Certainly it had something to do with his temperament. It was probably the kind of weapon that belongs to a god who rules the earth and the skies. Let me see...What was this thing he was going on about a while ago? Oh dear! My teachers are right about this. I am so absent minded. Oh yes! Now I remember: he was saying that he holds the power to mass clouds and bring about thunderstorms. Clouds...Thunderstorms...

Back on my screen, Typhon was this close to reaching the peak of the mountain. Zeus had withdrawn to its highest point, where thunderbolts were already tearing the sky apart.

That's it! Thunderbolts! With a single move, I swiped the thunderbolts above Zeus's head, and stuck them in his hand.

'At last you mortal boy! You woke up!'

Zeus hurled the thunderbolts at the monster at once. Most of the beast's heads were scorched, and these awful flames in their eyes died down. Typhon stepped back with a terrifying scream.

'More bolts you mortal boy! Give me more!'

One thing I am most proud of is my gaming skills! I was collecting and passing thunderbolts to Zeus non-stop! My fingers were on fire!

I have to admit: Zeus was hurling the bolts at each head with perfect accuracy. Like a proper machine gun. Typhon was slowly thrown off balance and, half-blind, he plummeted down the mountain. But then, he suddenly spread his wings open, and flew away from Olympus.

'Just in case I didn't mention before, you mortal boy: Typhon is a god, so he is immortal like me. I cannot kill him. If we want to overwhelm him, we must come up with a different solution.'

Zeus's reference to 'we' was rather flattering, but it made me feel very anxious! What now? Zeus took one long stride, and reached the western edge of Greece. From there, he flew over to Sicily, in the neighbouring country of Italy. I looked and noticed the massive volcano of Etna, bubbling and spitting out

lava in every direction. I see! This would be a good "seal" for Typhon, but could Zeus lift it?

'How little do you know the greatest god of all!'

Zeus literally uprooted the whole mountain at once, and held it over his head. Typhon was thrashing around, his snake-tails whipping the air.

'Mortal! Help me aim properly!'

Ok! That was easy! In the past, I have spent plenty of hours bumping angry little birds into bad pigs! I "grabbed" Etna (wow!) with my finger, I pulled it back like a slingshot, and then I shot it to Typhon! The volcano crushed the beastly creature with a terrific thud. Rivers of fiery hot lava poured from the depths of the earth, and covered the monster, leaving no trace of it. Just as it happens after a big earthquake, the earth was still shaking and moaning for a little while, until in the end everything calmed down.

Zeus looked at me under his thick eyebrows; I thought I noticed a tiny little smile under his heavy moustache.

'That was not bad at all, young mortal boy. The earth has now escaped Typhon's destructive forces. From time to time he will remind us of his presence with small shakes, and some other times he will be spitting out lava when trying to escape. But the worst has passed. I can now take some time to relax in my cloud palace above Mount Olympus. And you yourself can meet the rest of the family of the Olympian gods. It's about time I introduced you to the gang. I am sure there will be something there for you to do.'

Zeus flew away, and disappeared into the dark clouds while my tablet was vibrating from his thundering laughter.

DIVINE HEADACHE ON MOUNT OLYMPUS

The clouds cleared away, and the sun shone bright over a field covered in glistening crops. They were swaying in the wind like a golden carpet stretching out to the horizon. I swiped them with my finger, and they immediately responded to my move! Look at that! The "sea" of crops was then transformed into a real cloth! It was an astonishing spectacle to watch: it rose up into the air, and it embraced a beautiful woman with a well-proportioned, solid figure and strawberry blonde hair. She looked at me with her big hazel eyes.

'Well done, mortal boy. I saw how effectively you helped Zeus against Typhon. I am Demeter, the goddess of the earth and agriculture. I endowed humans with the grain, and I taught them how to cultivate it. Thanks to me, nature remains blossomed and fruitful. So I do owe you a debt of gratitude. Now that this turmoil has ceased, the earth can amply bestow its products.'

All of a sudden, loud claps of thunder started rumbling in the sky.

'Oh no! I can hear trouble coming from Olympus,' cried Demeter.

'I hope my sister Hera is not quarrelling again with her husband, Zeus the mighty. Hera is the wife of the king of the gods, the powerful queen of Olympus, and the patron of marriage and childbirth. But she is very jealous. Not without reason however: occasionally, Zeus is being charmed by other women - both goddesses and mortals...'

'Do gods have these kinds of problems too?' I thought, and Demeter smirked at me.

'Of course he always comes back to his beloved wife. But his disloyalty very often results in children that are not hers. A great deal of half-gods have been born like this; glorious heroes and rulers that stood out among humans. But my sister's wrath hunts both them and their mothers, and it is only the father of gods that can control it. I must go and find out what is the matter...'

I am not the gossipy type, but I was also dying to find out why Zeus was into such a stormy fury!

Demeter paused for a minute, and then thought aloud:

'No mortal has ever seen the cloud palaces atop the rocky mount of Olympus. You have met and helped Zeus however, so maybe we could make an exception this time. But you must bring a present with you...'

Demeter must have read my thoughts, because she looked at me with the look of surprise, and then burst into a loud laughter.

'Oh dear! No, not a present like the ones you modern people buy from the shops! What I really mean is something symbolic that will honour the gods; something that will represent your valuable effort. Oh, I have an idea!'

A sickle popped up on the right side of the screen. Demeter withdrew to a corner of the field, and winked at me. Surely she didn't want me to play Charon (that is the ferryman of the dead)! Instead, I slid the sickle on the crops, and started reaping the harvest. Once a bundle of grain stalks was made, the goddess gave me a nod of approval. With a single move, she separated the chaff from the grain, and formed a mound of pure wheat. Oh dear! Everything is so easy for gods! She then brought a pair of millstones placed on top of each other. Luckily, I had watched this documentary about farming in the old days! With one finger I started feeding seeds into the eye of the upper millstone, and with the other, I grabbed its wooden handle, and started spinning it around in order to grind the wheat. It was very difficult! I had to use all my strength. I thought the tablet screen would crack! Fortunately, I managed to gather plenty of flour in the end. Brilliant! That was a decent present, produced by pure physical work! A basic product symbolising human labour!

'Hey, boy! Don't be lazy! The earth endows you with her produce, so if you want to honour her, you must make something out of it,' said Demeter, while water, a clay bowl with a cloth, and a brick oven with a flat wooden shovel popped up on the side of the screen. Great! Am I supposed to be a baker now? What would my friends think if they saw me kneading dough - even a virtual one!

Demeter tried to hide a small grin.

If it wasn't for my immense curiosity to get a glimpse of the Olympian gods, I wouldn't really do this...So I decided to throw myself into work again. I knew I had to mix flour and water in the bowl, and then start the kneading. But how would I get the proportions right? Demeter and I started playing a game of signs: I was adding flour alternately with water, while Demeter was exclaiming 'more!' or 'enough!' sounds. In the end, following instructions from the goddess, I had to leave the dough to "sleep" and "rest" by covering the bowl with the cloth. Thankfully, she didn't ask me to tuck it in too!

'All right, all right. You can stop nagging. I won't let you wait for five hours, which is how long it actually takes for the dough to rise,' said Demeter, blowing towards the bowl. The dough emerged double in size, and the goddess fired the oven at once.

'Ready to bake!'

I used the shovel to place the dough in the hot oven. After some extra sign language, I managed to take the bread out, right on time. It was perfectly baked. I have to admit: my very first loaf of bread (in fact a digital loaf, but who cares) made me rather proud!

'Great! Now we can head towards the palace of Olympus,' said Demeter, taking the loaf with her. 'Follow me!'

Clouds cloaked the goddess, and lift her up.

What was I supposed to do? I scrolled up, looking for the goddess, and following the increasingly louder sound caused by the thunderstorms. Among them, I began to distinguish a deep masculine voice; it sounded like crying out in pain. Ultimately, in the depths of the horizon, amongst the thick clouds, I discerned the glistening tops of a dazzling golden palace. As I made my way through, the clouds became lighter and grew apart. A massive court emerged, with snow-white marble and sparkling columns dissolving into the clouds. I noticed many women and men around the gate. They were discussing with each other, and they seemed very concerned. They were definitely gods and goddesses. They all looked ageless and beautiful; their elegant bodies were dressed in light and delicate ancient Greek tunics. Women had their hair arranged in elaborate designs, and they had adorned themselves with precious golden jewels. But my attention was still drawn to these loud cries of pain, and the terrible thunderstorms rumbling from the depths of the palace. Great lightning was cracking across the sky, and two dark clouds remained fixed above the palace. For heaven's sake, what was happening to Zeus? What was that thing that made the immortal and all-powerful king of the gods suffer so much? Amongst all these divine figures, I picked out Demeter, who left the crowd and approached me. A magnificent dark-haired lady was with her. There was something royal about her, but her confidence barely concealed her anxiety. On the outside she seemed as tough as granite, but you could feel the lava of rage boiling inside her.

'Mortal boy, let me introduce you to Hera, the big boss of Olympus, Zeus's celebrated wife and dear sister of mine.'

My clumsy smile dropped. The cold and rigid goddess stared at me in suspicion, and inspected me with her piercing black eyes. I got the same goose bumps one gets when scraping a chalkboard! You could easily see why almighty Zeus had chosen this solemn goddess to be his formal wife. After what seemed like ages - while in fact it was just a few seconds of head-to-toe inspection - she finally spoke:

'My sister already told me about you, but don't get carried away. You are not supposed to be here! How about your parents? Do they know where you are, and what you are up to?'

I wasn't expecting this question. I started to mumble something, but Demeter intervened and saved me the trouble:

'But of course! Of course! He is a very respectful boy my dear sister, please don't treat him like this.' She then turned to me and quickly said: 'My sister, the goddess and patron of marriage and family, is always anxious about protecting and properly educating the young people,' then quickly turned to her sister and added: 'Look Hera, look what the mortal boy brought for us Olympians. A present he made all by himself...'

Hera looked at the loaf, and burst out a sarcastic laugh:

'Bread? Is it bread that this ignorant creature brought to the gods? To us, only eating the divine ambrosia, and only drinking the divine nectar?

One moment guys! Enough is enough! That's not fair! How am I supposed to know anything about ambrosias and nectars? Poor little me, I just did what Demeter asked!

Demeter rushed to patch things up:

'My dear Hera, I was the one who suggested this. I wanted the boy to show his respect for all these goods we gods are offering to the humans...'

Hera kept on looking at me firmly, but she softened a little:

'Anyway, I will give this to Hestia, the goddess of the hearth. She can place it on the palace's main altar. But I have no time for chit-chatting. Zeus is suffering from an agonising headache, and I don't know what to do. I have to be by his side. If you come across Hephaestus, please tell him his father is calling...'

Just before she left, I managed to catch a glimpse of her anguish; it was written all over her proud face. But what was really going on? Could gods get headaches? Could this be yet another jealousy scene?

'Yes to the first question, no to the second one,' Demeter responded to my thoughts. 'It is true that we gods are immortal and timeless, and that nothing can destroy us. But we are able to feel like humans do. As far as jealousy is concerned, this is an extremely complicated matter: you see Zeus's first wife was Metis, which means prudence. But when Zeus found out she was expecting his child, he shrunk her down, and swallowed her: he wanted to secure his rule from a dangerous successor, in fear of what an oracle - a prophecy - once predicted.'

This was truly horrible! The father of gods was losing my respect...

'You are a smart kid, mortal boy. After experiencing this adventure against Typhon, you must know by now that all these stories involving gods are very often of symbolic importance. When Zeus, his mind superior to all, "swallowed" prudence, he acquired the power to dispense good and evil forever. This is how he became the lord of justice, for both gods and humans...'

And what could possibly have happened to the child of Metis? In the end, I never got the chance to ask Demeter more details, because a woman emerged from the crowd of gods, and she was so beautiful, I became speechless. I was hypnotised. When she saw me like this, the woman burst out laughing.

Demeter sighed, and with a flat voice, she said:

'Aphrodite, let me introduce you to yet another one of your millions of admirers...,' and added: 'Mortal, this is rude, shut your mouth please. This is Aphrodite, the goddess of beauty and love...'

'I daresay this is my cutest fan of all! What a handsome young boy! And rather clever I've been told...,' she said with a silvery voice.

'Hey! Your blush is giving you away!' Demeter's voice jolted me from my slumber.

'Pl-pl-pleased to meet you!' (I can't stop giggling sometimes!)

Aphrodite turned to Demeter, and anxiously said:

'Zeus's agony is getting worse! He asked me to urgently get him Hephaestus. He thinks that he can do something about this headache. But my husband is hiding because he is really scared of how angry the father of gods is right now. Like a caged animal really! Mind you, Hephaestus must be locked in his workshop, but I am not going over there. You know how much I detest the soot and the heat of his kilns, but...,' she turned towards me full of joy, 'maybe this young mortal can persuade him. I've heard that the father of gods is really fond of him.'

'All right then! Come on young boy,' said Demeter, 'we will send you over to Hephaestus's workshop and I am sure you'll figure out something!'

Woah, woah, woah. One moment guys. Who is Hephaestus? What workshop? Aphrodite gave me another charming smile, and explained:

'My husband Hephaestus, son of Zeus and Hera, is the god of fire and metalworking, the finest of the blacksmiths and an excellent inventor. He has crafted bright golden thrones for the gods, but also unbreakable weapons and fabulous jewellery - all sorts of things really! I am sure that a talented boy like you will get on with him much better. I don't want to ruin my divine garments, for it would be such a pity...'

Before I could answer, the goddess filled the screen with smoke! As I was making my way through, I recognized a forge with incredible tools: huge anvils, several pairs of tongs, hammers and bellows. Amongst these, for the first time, I saw a fairly ugly god. He was extremely sturdy, with big muscular arms, thick black messy hair and a pair of bold eyebrows, with eyes as bright as fiery pieces of coal. He was covered in soot from head to toe, while sweat was dripping over his enormous muscles. Above all, I was impressed by the massive hammer he had in his hand: it was as big as his own head! By golly! How on earth could he lift this blasted thing? And whilst I was quite impressed already, I did notice something else too. Something rather unbelievable: the ugly god's helpers were a bunch of robots! Honestly! They were female robots, but made out of gold. You could tell they were lifeless objects, from their mechanical walking. Let's see...Having the prettiest goddess of all as a wife, and golden robots as maids...Not bad for a sooty man, lame in one leg!

'You mortal midget, do you want me to send you down to the Underworld where you can meet Hades, the god of the dead?' Hephaestus gave me a very serious, firm look.

Oh, for pity's sake! These gods can get all my thoughts...!

'Ehm, I do apologise Mr Hephaestus. Your wife and goddess Demeter have asked me to look for you. Your father needs you urgently...'

Hephaestus huffed. Huge flames gushed out of his kiln.

'I know, I know. It breaks my heart to see Zeus the almighty writhing in pain. But I can't do anything about this. I am not aware of any invention that heals headaches! Just a while ago actually, father went out of his mind. He asked me to chop his head open with the hammer! This is why I am hiding. I can't do such a thing...'

The god with the rock hard arms was now looking like a petty kid. I suddenly came up with something:

'Mr Hephaestus, if you would kindly take me to Zeus. I think I have an idea that might help. But can I ask you to take the hammer with you please...?'

Hephaestus looked at me suspiciously, but in the end he agreed:

'Listen, you mortal midget. I am not sure what you can do that all Olympian gods haven't already done. But I have to admit that I am desperate. Let us go, but you are taking full responsibility for this...'

My screen was once again filled with beautiful coral-pink clouds. A platform made of marble emerged in the centre, with bright golden thrones shining in the sun. Zeus, the one and only, was sitting on the main, most impressive one. He was holding his head in his hands, screaming so loud, that the divine palace was shaking as though there was an earthquake. A swarm of goddesses were coming and going, placing compresses of all sorts of magical herbs on his head, fanning him, and trying

to console him. Nothing could relieve him. The more his moaning grew, the more his terrible thunderbolts were ripping through the large and thick dark clouds.

Zeus noticed Hephaestus and, with a weak nod, he asked him to come close. At a pace too slow even for his crooked foot, Hephaestus approached him.

'Hephaestus my boy,' Zeus sighed, 'I can feel something in my head is fighting its way out. We've done all we could, but nothing works. You must open my head with one heavy hammer strike. Come on, don't hesitate. Do it...'

Hephaestus stood still, and mumbled:

'Father, pain is driving you out of your mind. I can't do this...'

Zeus shouted so loudly, that all the gods were paralysed with fear.

'I know very well what I'm talking about! I order you Hephaestus! Give me your hardest strike right NOW!'

The divine blacksmith was terrified. As mechanically as a robot, he lifted his massive hammer above his head, but stood there, as still as a statue. He was petrified with fear.

My moment had just come. I quickly swiped my finger and pulled the hammer towards Zeus's head, as hard as possible. The gods remained stunned. I held my breath.

Zeus stood still, gazing at me with bewilderment, until...

In no time, something unbelievable happened:

A dazzling ray of light shone out from the god's head, and every trace of cloud was suddenly gone. A figure sprang from within: a young woman with bold blue eyes. She was wearing a crested helmet, and she was holding a shield while aggressively wielding a spear. Before anyone could react, the young woman shouted a battle cry that shook the whole of Olympus. Everyone, but for Zeus, was again petrified. Despite the blow, the king of the gods emerged unscathed and relieved; he got up from his throne, and raised his hand towards the young woman.

'My daughter! Calm down dear! You are most welcome to the family of gods.'

The woman abandoned her shield and spear, and quietly sat next to him. Zeus then turned towards everyone else, and with his heavy voice announced:

'Let me introduce you to my daughter Athena, the goddess of wisdom. She will honour this divine generation with great deeds!' Everyone threw themselves into a cheerful applause. But Zeus himself fixed his eyes on me, and signalled everyone to quiet down.

Oh my! I choked up. Do you think he can actually throw thunderbolts through the screen?

'And now you...you rude mortal boy...did you just dare break the mighty king's head open?' (everyone, including me, held their breath) '...

well done!' he said at last, and a vague smile appeared under his beard. We all breathed a sigh of relief. Storm had passed.

The gods threw themselves into singing and dancing straight off. With a smile on her face, Athena was the first to give in. Only Hera seemed rather stiff while watching Metis's daughter, especially after such an unusual...birth!

Demeter came close, and carefully said:

'Boy, you just walked away with it! But tell me really: weren't you scared that you might harm Zeus?'

'Ms Demeter, you were the one who told me that the gods are immortal and deathless, and that nothing can beat them. So I already knew that Zeus wasn't really in danger!'

Demeter gave me the look of approval, and stepped into the dance.

While watching the celebrations, I thought:

'This means, that the father of all gods and humans, the god that stands for rational thought, "swallowed" prudence, and then, his mind "gave birth" to wisdom...Niiice!'

HOW TO SLAY THE PYTHON:
A "BRIGHT" IDEA!

I was thinking about goddess Athena, this wise warrior who had managed to utterly shake the palace of gods...I really wanted to get to know
her better. But suddenly...

My screen filled with the black messy hair and the black soot - that
is, the generally black head - of Hephaestus!

'Ah, you're still around? There is something we two should talk
about...'

Oh dear, I had forgotten all about him...I gulped, and waited for the
worst to come.

Could it be that he was still holding the super-hammer?

'Normally, little mortal bug, you would be in real trouble for having
put hands on an Olympian god without his permission - not to mention
in the presence of other gods... But judging from the outcome, I guess
I must thank you instead. The truth is that with this intervention, you
"saved" both me and Zeus. I was literally petrified. If it wasn't for you,

I would have ridiculed myself. Thank you, anyway. But don't take any initiative again!'

The enormous god was looking at me with his dark eyes. They were giving off some concealed affection. I gave him back my sweetest smile, and he faked a cold response:

'I received an order for invincible golden arrows from god Apollo. I must deliver as soon as possible. You can follow me to my workshop if you like.'

I didn't know who god Apollo was, but the phrase 'invincible arrows' was enough of bait for me to take!

Once again, my screen filled with the familiar black smoke coming from the god's forge. But once this settled, we came across something unexpected: the god's golden maids had been pretty much torn into pieces! Most of their golden parts had been unscrewed, while their metallic hands and legs were strewn all over the floor. The workshop looked like a warehouse of broken shop-window mannequins...

'Golly! What happened here? It could be that Athena's loud cry, and the heavy shake that followed, detuned them, and made their screws go loose...How annoying! I now have to put off the order, until I fit them back together...'

Hmm...Maybe I could give him a hand.

Hephaestus immediately heard my thought, and turned to me with a friendly look.

'Of course, you have my permission to help! But be careful. Screwing the torn pieces back together requires high attention to detail. You see, every robot is unique in design and in size. This means you have to match each maid, with the correct parts. Here, take this special screwing tool...'

Something like a screwdriver popped up on the side of the screen. I grabbed it right away, and got down to work. It was so much fun! In actual fact, I was dealing with a large, three dimensional puzzle! For each piece, there was only one matching position. Luckily, the fact that there was an individual design for each robot, it helped a lot. Well...as much as I hate bragging about it, solving puzzles is my forte! In a short while, the classy metallic maids were fully restored.

Hephaestus inspected them, looking satisfied in the end.

'Well done, mortal boy! Good job. Now you can run one more errand for me: can you please take these golden arrows, and give them to Apollo...?' Before I could answer, he laughed and added:

'Don't hesitate, you will immediately recognise him. He is the most sensational god; he really can't go unnoticed...'

Hephaestus left the arrows in the corner of the screen, and then, the scene changed once again. The gate leading to the divine palaces re-appeared through the clouds, and a dazzling glow shined through. The glow came so close, that I couldn't keep my eyes on the tablet anymore.

'I forgot you are a mortal, young man,' said the shining, 'let me re-duce my glare a little bit, so you can see me...'

The light softened, and a breath-taking golden chariot emerged, drawn by big, snow-white swans, and driven by an extremely handsome young man. He had blond curly hair, held together by a golden ribbon. A short chlamys was covering his well-proportioned figure. Like a fool, I stood there, staring at the chariot and the bright god, one after anoth-er. In the end, I thought, who cares about stupid one-seat sports cars! That's a device that can drive you everywhere in style!

'Hey mortal, you like my chariot, eh? So do I! It's a present from my father! Zeus! I am glad we have the chance to meet, you know. I am Apollo, also known as Phoebus, the god of light. Oh! And of truth, and music, and the rest of the fine arts, and harmony, and prophecy, and healing...Anyway, to cut a long story short, I am what I am!'

I myself realised that my mouth was still wide open, and I quickly snapped it shut. I remembered the Aphrodite incident, so I didn't want to start giggling again...!

'I am glad too,' I said simply, and secretly thought, 'and I regret I didn't take any sunglasses with me!'

Apollo laughed warmly.

'You are not just bold and fearless, young mortal. You have a good

sense of humour too! I like you already! So! Do you have something for me?' he said, and nodded towards the empty quiver hanging from his shoulder.

'Of course! Your order is rrrright here! Invincible golden arrows, as made by Mr Hephaestus...' I grabbed the arrows from the corner of the screen, and placed them in his quiver. Hmm... I was dying of curiosity. These lethal arrows were destined for someone...I wanted to find out who this poor creature was.

'It's a horrific dragon called Python. Hera had sent him out to stop my mother, Leto, from giving birth to me, and my twin sister, Artemis, the goddess of the moon, hunt and the forests.'

I see! Yet another one of Zeus's little adventures...that added more glorious members to the divine family tree.

'I just found out that the Python is hiding in a cave at Delphi. He is terrorising the local residents,' added Apollo. 'Listen. This is my chance. Would you really like to give a hand? I would think that a massive snake wouldn't frighten you after Typhon, eh?'

The invite was challenging and tempting.

'Mr Apollo, I am following your highness...'

Apollo's swans flapped their wings vigorously, and the golden chariot launched into the clouds. Its shadow bounded over high hills, lush green valleys and sparkling seas far below. I could hear the wind rumbling in my ears. It felt like I was holding the reins. What a marvellous flight! Better than any journey by plane! In the end, a big mountain appeared just below.

'Here we are, on the slopes of Mount Parnassus,' said Apollo, and landed his chariot on a small plain. As we approached, I noticed the opening of a wide dark cave. I hurriedly "ran" my finger towards it, to get a better glimpse.

'One moment mortal. We can't do anything in this darkness.'

Apollo reached the opening of the cave, and released a flow of light. It was so bright, that I wasn't able to distinguish more than his silhouette. Its penetrating beams reached every single dark corner. Wait a minute. The serpent monster was nowhere to be seen. I could only see the cave's walls, with their big round rocks glistening with moisture.

'The rocks are the monster, young boy!' exclaimed Apollo, and all at once, he grabbed a golden arrow from his quiver, and placed it on his bow. The cave's shape was instantly transformed. Under the blinding light, the "walls" started to shift around. Python's enormous body had completely covered the whole of the cave! The rocks that I saw were nothing but the large curves of his coiled body.

'Mortal, there is no time to waste. I must shoot straight into the snake's mouth. His thick skin is totally arrow-proof. So make sure you keep an eye out for the moment his head shows up. When his mouth opens, I want you to help me point accurately...'

At some stage, we need to talk about this habit gods have...of mentioning very important details at the very last minute, I mean! Anyway, I didn't want to give up now. The actual god of light was expecting

my help! I tangled my fingers together, and I stretched them to crack my knuckles.

'I'm ready!' I said, or at least, so I thought...

The enormous snake was moving around with remarkable flexibility. It was impossible to tell between the head and the tail.

Suddenly, its head appeared in one of the corners. I used my finger to try and position the arrow in the correct angle. The arrow was released with great force, but reached its target only after the beast had just hid its head.

The god placed another arrow on his bow, and stood there waiting. After a while, the head popped up again, but in a whole different spot. Oh, boy! This venture was even more difficult than trapping Typhon beneath Etna! I tried to aim again. The arrow whizzed through the air, but Python's head had already disappeared. We tried again and again. Apollo also tried shooting without my help, but with no success. Each time, the dragon popped up in different spots; sometimes near the top, sometimes near the bottom, then on the right, then on the left, deep inside the cave, or at the front, near its opening. After several attempts Apollo became desperate. There was only one arrow left in his divine quiver. We had one last shot, and there was no light at the end of this tunnel... Wait a minute! That's it! No light! There should have been no light...

I shared my idea with the god, and he approved.

'All right! Let's do it!' he answered passionately.

Apollo "turned off" his light completely, and perched the last arrow on his bow. I used my finger to hold it in place, and stayed there in full alert. We had to wait like this for a little while: entirely motionless in the complete darkness, until the dragon thought we had given up. Unless he felt the threat was over, he wouldn't calm down and come forward.

Indeed, a few minutes later we heard some slithering. We felt the beast's breath making its way in the heavy darkness. Strangely enough, even I could smell his breath stinking up near me!

'NOW!' exclaimed Apollo, while releasing his bright glow throughout the cave. Next thing I knew, Python's frightening head was right there in front of us. Apollo's light flashed like a camera shot and stunned the monster. With its mouth wide open, it stayed there unable to move. In the blink of an eye, I raised my finger and the god re-leased the bowstring. Hephaestus's last invincible arrow pierced the gaping dragon's neck. Python screamed of terror. He was writhing with fury, lashing his enormous tail right and left. The cave's walls were shaking so hard, that I thought it was about to collapse. After a while, the dragon finally fell on the ground, and surrendered to death.

Apollo then said: 'We made it young mortal! Thanks to your help this land's fortune will now change forever.'

Well, I'm telling you, it was worth it. Getting rid of such a horrific beast can't be a small thing!

'That's not what I mean,' the god answered back. 'This land, Delphi, is a sacred place with special

powers. I'll tell you what. When my father Zeus decided to locate the centre of the world, he released two eagles at opposite ends. The eagles flew across the earth, and met here, at Delphi. This is why this place is called "the navel" of the earth. As the god of prophecy, I will establish here the greatest shrine of all; a place where people will come to ask for guidance and to learn of the future. I will appoint an oracle, a priestess, who will be named Pythia, to remind us of the Python, who used to live here.'

A priestess - fortune teller! Very interesting. I am sure there are plenty of people, who would like to know what will happen to them.

'The oracle's prophecies will be unclear. Pythia will only give a hint; a certain approach to each subject. People too must use their minds - just like you did a while ago. Anyway, all these belong to the future. For the time being, let us go for a ride in my chariot. It will help us forget all about Python's smelly breath!'

The shiny god ordered his swans to spread their wings.

We left Delphi behind, and we flew over remote fields. In the end, we landed on a large green farm. Flowers of all kinds of sizes, evergreens, hedges and herbs, all made up a charming colourful painting.

'That's it, mortal. I am heading off now. This is Pieria: my favourite cows are grazing here. I must start organising the structure of my oracle. I am certain we will meet again though. Until then, remember: cleverness is just a power. You yourself will be deciding if you will use it for a good or for a bad purpose...'

Was Apollo - the bright and the all-knowing god - trying to tell me something? Ah, well. We'll find out!

THE WINGED RASCAL
AND APOLLO'S COWS

I was gazing at the beautiful countryside and the cows idly grazing in the field. I could see them swishing their tails back and forth to swat away the irritating flies, and I noticed that they were actually chewing in complete unison. As if they had surrendered to some mysterious musical rhythm. That's it! These cows were...rapping!

I laughed at my own thoughts, when all of a sudden...

'Hey! Mortal boy!' A tiny head with bright golden locks, and a pair of wily little eyes popped up in the tablet's bottom corner.

'Don't you have anything better to do than just staring at cows?' said the boy, and jumped forward offering a dramatic bow.

'I am Hermes, the super-god! Hats off to your highness!' he said. The boy seemed a little younger than me.

'I am only a few days old! Ah well! We gods grow at our own rate! I will soon reach the peak of my youth. And there I will remain forever, for I am immortal,' he said, performing a funny jump by clapping his feet together.

Taken aback, I was unable to speak in time, and so he added:

'You don't know me, I know. That's alright. I do know you. It looks like my father, Zeus, and some other Olympian gods really like you. I beg your pardon, but to me you look a little foolish!'

Foolish? That took a lot of nerve; I had had enough of this. God or no god, he had it coming! I was about to open my mouth and give him a piece of my mind, but that rude boy stopped me:

'Please don't be cross with me my mortal friend. I know that you do have the brains and the bravery. But the thing is, wouldn't you want to do something without approval from the grown-ups? Something daring or even something, say, crazy!'

But, I thought, how about tossing volcanoes, fixing golden robots or killing dragons? Aren't these daring enough?

'Oh come on, as if you don't get it...I don't mean great deeds. What I am talking about is a crafty prank.'

'And what kind of a crafty prank do you have in mind, Mr Hermes?' I asked suspiciously.

'Well, these cows belonging to Apollo for example...I am sure you know how my older brother has prophetic skills, which is why no one can really hide anything from him. Wouldn't it be fun if we manage to make his cows "disappear" so that he can't find them? Plus, we could make it impossible for him to blame us.'

Something inside me warned me this was a bad idea: 'Attention, trouble ahead.' But before I could express my objections to Hermes, he spoke again:

'Of course nothing will happen to the cows and in the end we will return them back to their owner!'

'I don't think it's a good idea to anger a god for no reason,' I said firmly.

'There you are! This is why I call you a fool...!' he said, and lay down on the grass crossing his hands on his chest as if he didn't care.

Well no! I had to take a stand for myself. I wouldn't let that mouthy boy say the last word!

'Ok then nursery god, tell us, is there a plan for this...crafty prank you just came up with?'

Hermes jumped up like a grasshopper.

'Of course there is! I will take these cows and hide them elsewhere, in a cave I have found.'

'That's not a plan,' I said. 'That's silly. Even if you have the skills to herd and control fifty cows, their tracks will lead Apollo straight to that cave!'

'Not if the tracks lead over here!' Hermes answered in triumph and then started dancing a perky dance of his own, as if he was a frog walking on coal.

Despite my concerns, curiosity got the better of me and forced me to ask him:

'And how do you intend to make the cows' tracks go over here while they will actually be going over there? Do you perhaps hold a magic wand?'

Hermes stopped his dance and pressed his freckled nose against the screen of the tablet. His voice turned low and secretive:

'I don't need a magic wand. I will have them walk...backwards!'

I have to admit, that mischievous god was fun! And quite imaginative! So I pretended to believe him and I asked:

'Ok, fair enough, the cows will be walking backwards. How about your own trail, how are you going to erase that? Do you also have the ability to fly?'

His two wily eyes gave me a long stare:

'You haven't thought about that, eh? Well, this "fool" of a boy did think about it,' I said, and that shut him up!

For a few seconds Hermes didn't seem to respond. He then leant towards me again, and attempted to flatter me by saying:

'All right then my noble fellow. If you tell me how to erase my tracks, I will not let anyone call you a fool ever again!'

What could I say to this? Actually, I knew very well what to say. I answered back:

'If you manage to make the cows walk backwards, then I will tell you how to erase your tracks...'

What a mistake! What a huge mistake! We should never ask a god, no matter how big, no matter how small, to do something difficult...

Before I was able to withdraw my proposal, Hermes had shot off, running around the cows like a dog herding the cattle. He then grabbed a long stick in each hand, and by walking up and down, he set about aligning the bulky animals. He was commanding them in gibberish, with shrill whistles and many funny sounds. It all worked perfectly! Not bad for a new-born baby! In the end the cows lined up quietly in ten groups of five; just like school kids!

Hermes then turned around, and gave me a pompous look. With the sticks in his hands, and the serious manner of a professional conductor, he started guiding the cows' reverse walk. They obeyed, and started walking backwards as if performing in a circus act...

'How about now my fellow, eh? Now do you believe me?' He didn't wait for an answer and added: 'Let us wait for your solution now...'

He winked at me cunningly. I had fallen into the trap. What now? I was just realising that this little sneaky god had a special gift for persuading both animals and humans. I sighed, and thought that since he had actually managed to put a whole herd of cows "into reverse", surely he could also win round Apollo. So I tried to set my hesitations aside, and I focused really hard on the screen, looking for a solution to the Hermes-and-his-trail problem. My mind travelled to a cowboy movie where I had seen tracks wiped out with tree branches. But I didn't really feel like following each step the baby god was taking and "wiping" every single one of his tracks behind him - this could take ages!

With my finger, I plucked off some leaves from the surrounding bushes and put them under Hermes's feet. Then, I grasped some flexible stems and fixed them on the leaves to keep them in place. Hermes was excited with his new wacky pair of shoes. He started walking up and down to check if any tracks were left behind him.

'Perfect! Thank you, my noble fellow! You are very skilful indeed! I will now set about hiding the cows in the cave. This is sooo much fun!'

The little rascal started driving the cows backwards, until they dropped out of sight.

After a while Hermes returned:

'Mission accomplished! The cows are well hidden in the cave, and all tracks lead here! I can't wait to see my brother's face when he sees the footprints without their cows!'

Well, I can wait myself, I thought, but I was at once distracted by something strange the little god was holding. It reminded me of a tortoise shell.

'That's right! It is the hollow shell of a tortoise! I was really bored on my way back here. I happened upon this empty shell, I grabbed it, and I stretched these strings across it. They come from animal gut and... listen...'

Hermes plucked the strings with his fingers; they released a wonderful sound. That little handyman had just made an unconventional lyre!

'Well done! It sounds very nice!' I said, but he seemed rather frightened all of a sudden.

'I can hear my brother, he is on his way! Be careful you mortal thing,

don't say a word!'
Hermes hid the lyre under his chlamys, and started whistling and feigning innocence.
At once, the screen filled with the familiar dazzling light. When the glow softened, I saw the handsome god pulling Hermes's ear. It wasn't difficult to understand, the scene spoke for itself: 'having sooo much fun' would not be an option anymore...

'You naughty thief. You little troublemaker. How come you already started playing tricks, eh? You are still a baby!' Apollo was yelling at him. 'You thought I wouldn't figure out that you are the one who hid my cows? Come on! Speak! Where are they?'

Hermes faked the most innocent expression in the whole world. He was trying to reassure Apollo that he didn't know where his cows were.

'Let's go on trial to Zeus's court! The fair judge of all gods and humans will teach you a lesson...'

On trial? This was getting serious. Wait a minute. Apollo ignored me completely. Did I just get away with it? The bright god jumped into his chariot without stopping pulling Hermes's ear, and took off.

I was anxiously waiting to see what or who was now going to show up on the screen. The familiar Olympian palaces re-emerged through the clouds, and the golden throne of the first of the gods glowed brightly. Zeus was leaning forwards, carefully listening to Apollo and Hermes who were arguing loudly.

'Father,' said Apollo, 'it's a profound theft we are talking about here. Hermes knew that these are my cows, and yet he stole them from me. And now, he of course pretends he knows nothing about it, and he doesn't tell me where they are.'

Hermes was playing innocent. He was passionately denying all accusations: a great performance. The path for a career in theatre was well-paved for the little god!

A sudden move of Zeus's hand was enough to stop them talking. He turned around, and looked me in the eyes. He said nothing, he just stared at me. This was too much for me to take, and I glanced down.

Suddenly, big dark clouds torn by strong lighting clustered above Zeus. The king of the gods rose up. His eyes were flashing with anger. That's it. No more jokes.

'Hermes you are a thief and a liar! You disrespected both your brother and me. You deserve the toughest of punishments...' Zeus raged at him.

Hermes abandoned his acting performance, and kept quiet. He was now nothing more than a little frightened kid.

'Excuse me, one moment please...' I heard myself saying. 'Mr Zeus, I don't mean to be nosy or anything, but I am sure Hermes did what he did because he just wanted to have some fun. He didn't have bad intentions...'

Zeus and Apollo looked at me in surprise.

'And how can you be so sure about that, mortal?' asked the Olympian king.

It was about time I assumed some responsibility for this.

'I am sure, because I was there and I helped him...' I said and waited for a second round of rage.

But instead, I saw Zeus and Apollo exchanging a knowing look. They almost smiled. Then Zeus turned towards Hermes, and said:

'Hermes, you are smart, but not as smart as you may think. You should know that...' he looked at me through the corner of his eyes, 'nothing can be kept secret from the father of gods. As someone rightly said, we must use our powers for a good purpose...Anyway, I will end by saying this: you know what you did was wrong. You must immediately bring your brother's cows back, and then apologise. He will then have to decide what kind of punishment you will receive...'

I couldn't believe I was butting in again. What was the matter with me?

'Mr Apollo. Before you punish him, I think you must see this; your brother has a present for you...' I said and nodded at Hermes, who was looking completely flustered and needed to wake up.

'Ehm, yes! Of course! I made this with my own two hands and I am offering it to you my dear brother! You are the god of music after all, so it suits you better.' Good old Hermes had recovered. He took the lyre out from under his chlamys, and with a dramatic gesture he offered it to Apollo. The god of light was a bit reluctant to start with. He took it, and touched the strings with his hands. The lyre's delightful sound spread out all around the palaces, and the eyes of the bright god glowed even stronger. He and Zeus smiled.

'Thank you Hermes,' said the bright god. 'Your present is marvellous. Come on now. Off we go. You need to show me where my cows are.'

Apollo seemed very happy with me. He and Hermes left.

When we were left alone, Zeus said to me:

'I daresay, young mortal, you made it again. You are honest and forthright. This is very important. So remember: always listen to your inner "voices".' He smiled under his thick beard.

My screen became covered with clouds and the heavenly palaces disappeared. After a little while, the clouds seemed lighter, and I saw the familiar countryside with Apollo's cows once again quietly grazing in the field. A young man landed in front of me in a rather spectacular way. He had a cape tied all around his neck. On his head, he had a bizarre leather hat with two feathers, and he was wearing winged sandals. He was holding something like a wand: it was a wooden staff entwined with two snakes, whose heads were facing each other. But wait a minute. I can see golden locks under that hat...and these wily eyes...they remind me of something...

'Hermes?'

'That's me mortal! I told you: we gods grow at our own unusual rate. So, here I am. The final version of me! What do you think of my new... accessories?'

I couldn't get a word in before he went on:

'After I apologised to my brother, and after I returned his cows back to him, my father proclaimed me the god of oratory, diplomacy and trade. On top of that, I will also be the patron of thieves, but I will also protect the righteous from the crooks! Nice, eh? I will also be considered the official messenger of the gods: I will carry gods' commands to the humans. Which is why I am wearing this special hat called petasus as well as these winged sandals! One more thing: I will guide people's dead souls down to the Underworld, the kingdom of Hades. So, what do you think? How do I look?'

There we go kid! Well done! But what was this wand?

'Whilst returning Apollo's cows, I did a good deed: I came across two fighting snakes and I managed to separate them. Zeus then gave me this magic wand, the herald's staff, to use it against discord amongst people.'

I was impressed. All of these roles suited the young god perfectly! Hermes smiled, and quietly added:

'By the way, I would like to thank you for defending me in front of Zeus. It took some bravery to do what you did. And this trick with the lyre was pretty amazing: my brother is so excited about it, he didn't even punish me! I have to say, you are not foolish at all!'

'Thank you Hermes. I hope you will stay away from dangerous tricks...don't get into any trouble from now on'

'Are you insane? With all these new gadgets I can come up with even better pranks! Besides, I am not worried about getting into trouble. Apart from being a good trickster, I am also good at choosing nice friends...' Hermes gave me a mischievous wink, and after offering a dramatic bow in the air, he flew up towards Olympus...

What can you say to that?

ATHENS: A GREAT CITY, A DIVINE QUARREL

The scene of the peaceful countryside remained on the screen. An owl's persistent hoot could be heard from a tree. I was always fond of this animal. It has a funny way of looking at you, blinking only one of its two large eyes, as if it's trying to tell you something secretively. Also, I think it's very interesting how it can twist its head a full 360°! This makes it capable of seeing things in every direction, which is a great advantage I find.

The persistent hoot became even stronger, until a charming owl emerged through the green foliage. It came close and gently tapped on the screen with its beak, still looking at me mysteriously. Oh! Now I see. The hoot was for me!

The owl flew away and I "followed" it. After a short flight, we came across a beautiful ancient city, a polis, just like the one Zeus had once shown me. It was sprawling across a plain surrounded by lush green mountains. To the south, the city opened up to the sea. It was flanked by two long rivers, and its central point was a green hill, on top of a high rocky outcrop. The owl flew towards there. When it reached over the highest point, it swept down and gently landed on the shoulder of a beautiful female silhouette. I couldn't see more than her outline because she was facing the sun. The young woman was wearing a helmet and a full-length chiton. Her hand was leaning on a long spear, and with the other, she was covering her eyes against the sun. She was gazing into the horizon along the city's outskirts, where the sun glittered upon the sea. Her posture reflected her serene and powerful nature. Without even turning around, she said:

'I sent out my sacred bird for you because you have expressed a desire to meet me. This is a good opportunity, I think...'

The young woman turned around and smiled at me.

It was Athena!

'I am honoured!' I exclaimed. Her eyes were mesmerising: now that I had the chance to take a close look at them, I couldn't help but admire their exceptional glow. Their colour was deep-blue like sea at its calmest, while her bronze-blonde hair was gleaming in the sun under her large helmet. Wait a minute. Is the goddess of wisdom a warrior too? What a bizarre combination...

'I am both, young mortal. But please, do not misunderstand. I am not full of lust for battle like my brother Ares, the god of war, and I don't take any pleasure in watching mortals falling dead on to the blood-soaked ground. I am a friend of peace and to those who favour it, I inspire wonderful achievements. But, in order to protect peace's gifts and defend justice, I must fight rather frequently. This means I am always, so to speak...peacefully prepared for war.'

I remember the earthquake that caused her battle cry, and I thought that nobody would ever want to anger her.

'The greatest power doesn't lie within physical strength, mortal, but within the mind. I am teaching humans that it's not always the strongest who wins; it is the smartest and the most reasonable.'

That's right! But what was Athena doing in this beautiful place?

'It is here that the most powerful city of Greece will flourish, mortal.

Its people will accomplish wonderful things, the glory of which will last forever. This is why I wish to take it under my wing. I am aiming to become the city's patroness.'

'You reckon without the host, my niece...without me!' echoed a voice as loud as rumbling thunder. An imposing bearded man with thick, messy hair and a large golden trident made his appearance in front of Athena. 'I, famous Poseidon, Zeus's brother, god of the sea, the rivers and the springs, I own the right to make this city mine. A single glance at the surrounding rivers and the sea should be enough to persuade you...'

Is the god of the sea also claiming this city? Things are getting complicated...

'Esteemed Poseidon,' said Athena calmly but firmly, 'I do apologise, but you are a little late. I was the first to claim this place. I am sure another great city would be honoured to have you as its patron.'

'How dare you answer me back? You know very well that I, together with your father and Hades, we are the Big Three gods, the ones who govern the Skyworld, the Waterworld and the Underworld...'

'First of all, Poseidon, only Zeus is the greatest of all gods and humans. Also, you too know very well that the earth belongs to all gods, and that I was the first to cast my divine shadow on this part of the world,' Athena argued firmly.

'By a thousand dolphins! My own divine shadow is the greatest of them all!' furious Poseidon roared and scared the owl away from Athena's shoulder.

Wow! A storm was brewing! Neither of the two gods seemed willing to step back and I was in the middle of a dispute between two gods. How interesting!

'There you are! We have looked for you in every corner of the museum!' my mother's voice made me jump. My parents were standing over me. I had completely forgotten about them! I can't believe this! Why did they have to find me now? All these amazing things were just happening...

'I can't believe my eyes! We are surrounded by all these wonderful objects and you prefer playing games on the tablet?' mum said whilst looking at my screen with disdain.

I quickly tucked it away under my arm.

'No, you see, wait, I...I am watching this very interesting documentary drama about Greek mythology,' I managed to come up with a reasonable excuse.

'That's my boy,' said my dad, 'this is the best way to learn more about the ancient Greek civilization!'

'How about you? What are you up to? Did you finish? Do we have to leave?' I asked as if I didn't care.

'Not really! There is more to see. We would normally need two days to properly explore everything in this museum. Why? Are you tired? Do you want us to leave?' mum asked me.

No I don't! All I wanted from them was to leave me alone! I wanted to find out what these gods were about to do! Of course I couldn't confess any of these things to my parents without them having to get me this special little jacket with the cute sleeves that nicely tie hands together behind the back! I didn't want them to think I was crazy, so I decided to play innocent.

'No, I am not tired, not at all! I can wait for as long as you need. Take your time!'

'Fantastic! It would be a shame if we had to leave and then come back,' mum said. 'There is a very nice garden café just downstairs. We can take a short break over there until we carry on. Is that all right?'

Dad and I agreed. We went down the museum stairs and we found the café. I was trying to stay behind and get quick glimpses of the two gods fighting on the screen. The situation was only getting worse! Athena and Poseidon had now relocated in front of the throne of the great ruler, and they were arguing very aggressively! It looked like they had turned to Zeus for a fair solution.

We all sat down in the garden. The setting was truly pretty, but I was dying to know what was happening! What was I missing? Who was to win the city? Would the two of them have to battle? I was responding to my parents passively. The gods were sticking in my mind.

At last, my parents left the café and went upstairs to the main section of the museum where they could continue with their visit. I told them I was going to remain there, because I was supposedly going through some learning material on the web, something which was not a lie really, since this adventure with the gods was very much educational indeed! (Dear me! I just did an "Hermes"!)

Anyway, as soon as they disappeared from view, I took the tablet out and I looked at it in excitement.

Athena and Poseidon were back on the city's central hill. But this time, there was another strange man standing next to them. He was wearing something like a crown on his head, and his bottom half was some sort of serpent. A large crowd of people were gathered around them. They must have been the city's residents. While Poseidon was busy talking to the man-serpent, Athena took the chance to carefully come close to the screen.

'Don't worry mortal, I know you were busy...Here is the situation so far: Poseidon and I couldn't work things out so we turned to Zeus for a solution. He suggested going to Cecrops, the man-serpent and founder of this city as well as its residents. It is up to them now to pick their patron-god. Each of us will have to present a gift. The victor will be whoever provides the city with the most useful one.'

Zeus had once again given a fair and clever solution! I didn't have the chance to say anything to Athena because Poseidon's rumbling voice was heard saying:

'I will present the people of this city with a gift that will be useful during peacetime and wartime!' At once he struck the rock in front of him with his golden trident, and a wonderful pure white horse sprang from within. Cecrops and the rest of the people were stunned at the sight of this jaw-dropping spectacle.

'Esteemed Poseidon,' exclaimed the king, 'your gift is wonderful! What do you call this wonderful animal?'

'It is called "horse". It can quickly take you anywhere you like. You can load it or ride it in battle, and it is useful for farming too,' Poseidon answered proudly.

The crowds were charmed by the god's gift. Poseidon looked at Athena with disdain. The beautiful goddess seemed baffled. She quietly said to me:

'Young mortal, now is a good time to show me how famously sharp you are! I would like to provide these people with a peace-gift; some-

thing whose value will remain unchanged throughout the centuries. But not gold or wealth, both of which will cause discord and war amongst them. What I am looking for is a precious, but at the same time humble product of nature; something of sustenance for the rich and the poor alike.'

I felt desperate. What could I possibly know about Greece and these people separated from us by thousands of years? And what is it that has a true eternal value? I opened my eyes and looked around anxiously for some kind of idea. In the meantime, little birds were cheerfully chirping in the trees of the little green garden café. The breeze was rustling through a couple of old gnarled olive trees. Their swaying leaves were shimmering under the sunlight and their little fruits were glinting like beads of green and gold. But then…something sparkled…in my mind! I had an idea!

The olive tree! This humble plant is a centuries-old source for precious fine oil, also known as the "green gold"! The basic ingredient for a healthy diet!

Athena looked at me and her deep-blue eyes twinkled. She turned towards Cecrops and the crowd, and proudly announced:
'This is my gift!'
With a single move she struck her spear into the ground. The rock split open,

and revealed a lush olive tree which grew and bore fruit at once.

The people fell silent.

'Wise Athena,' Cecrops asked at last, 'what could this tree offer us?'

'This is an olive tree. It can live for centuries, and it can grow in poor and dry soil without any water or much care. From its fruit you can extract oil; a precious, nourishing and healthy food that will help you live longer. Oil will also make your meals tastier. It will light your lamps and it will heal your wounds. One more thing: wreaths of olive leaves will crown with glory all the winners of the most notable competition, the Olympic Games. The olive tree branch will be the symbol of eternal peace.'

Cecrops and the rest of the people erupted in cheers. Everyone was praising the wise goddess, and implored her to become the city's patroness. Athena was - obviously - the victor of this extraordinary contest.

But suddenly a booming voice silenced everyone. Poseidon, his eyes flashing with flames of anger, raised his trident with menace:

'You are all fools. Let me now give you a gift you truly deserve!' he shouted and at once pointed his trident towards the sea near the horizon. The sea's calm blue surface turned into a boiling dark mass. Enormous rough waves erupted and crashed on to the shore, their force overwhelming the fields surrounding the city.

'Stop it, Poseidon!' Athena shouted. 'People were free to choose and you must respect their decision!'

It was pointless. The god of the sea sniggered, whilst the sea level continued to rise alarmingly.

'Come on mortal!

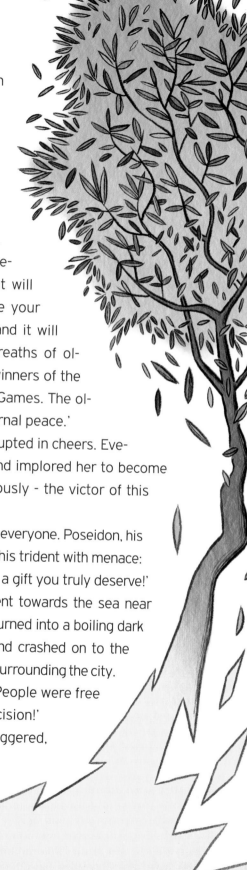

Quick! You must do something to prevent the water from flooding the city. In the meantime, I will ask my father to stop Poseidon,' said Athena, and vanished.

Sure, why not? Piece of cake! ...How on earth was I supposed to stop a tsunami from flooding a city? I had no choice: I carefully went through the screen again. I tried to re-examine the rocky hill in the centre of the city. Zilch. Nothing but rocks.

Rocks? But of course! This could be the solution! I used my finger to pull out rocks from the slopes of the outcrop, and I began piling them around the city, as if I were building a giant fortress. But I had to be extremely quick with this because the water was thundering over every single corner of the city, overwhelming everything in its path. Luckily, I managed to somehow build a low embankment. It looked like this impromptu wall was doing the job. I had saved some time but I was now running out of rocks! In a few seconds the sea would manage to break through my barrier and cover the whole of the city.

I ignored etiquette and all kinds of formalities and desperately cried, 'Athena!'

Suddenly a terrific thunderbolt tore the sky apart, and struck right next to Poseidon, causing the rocky hill to shake altogether. Athena turned up next to the god of the sea, and smoothly said:

'This, uncle, is Zeus's message to you I believe...'

Poseidon didn't respond. He simply raised his trident in the air and vanished. The seawater immediately withdrew, and once again it turned into a soft silvery-blue carpet extending all the way to the horizon. Everyone felt relieved and started thanking the goddess. Her owl returned and gently swept down onto her shoulder, gazing over the ecstatic crowd.

Athena waved her arm to the people to silence them:

'Mortals, I thank you for this honour. As your patroness, I am giving this city my name. From now on, it will be called Athens. This name will bring great glory and long-lasting recognition to your city.'

'Goddess Athena,' exclaimed Cecrops, 'in return, we will honour

you by erecting a glorious temple, the Parthenon, on the Acropolis, the edge - the acron - of your polis. It will be dedicated to you, our virgin patroness. One more thing: your mortal assistant gave me another brilliant idea. We will construct strong walls around Athens to protect it from its enemies!'

Athena nodded in satisfaction, and turned towards the crowd:

'My beloved Athenians. Today we learned that all mortals are capable of great deeds as long as they are ready to make decisions and use their mind...' She then smiled at me through the corner of her eyes. The owl on her shoulder twisted its head a 180°, and winked at me!

THE LOOK THAT TURNS YOU INTO STONE

The goddess was veiled by a blanket of clouds.

'Young boy! Time to get ready for some fresh adventures! You will meet a mortal that will need your help. I know I can count on you,' said Athena, and then vanished.

I was immensely proud of myself! The goddess of wisdom was counting on me? Not bad...

'Hey, mate! Why don't you "come down to earth" for a little while? Follow me!' Hermes's playful voice brought me back to reality. The winged god was all smiles, but an overcast gloomy sky was creeping up behind him. When the dark clouds cleared, an appalling scene was revealed; one with black marshes spewing out smoke, and muddy wetlands smothered in terrible shadows. Hermes pushed aside a few thick shrubs, and a young strong man came into view. He was kneeling down, watching something. The god answered my questions before I had a chance to ask them:

'Exactly, that's the guy you should help. And yes, both Athena and I are part of this game. And no, you don't really need to know anything else! Just give him these, when the time comes...' he announced, and - in the usual dramatic fashion - he revealed a shiny copper shield, and a curved golden sword, both of which he dropped on the side of the screen.

'The sword is mine and can be thrust into anything. And don't lose this shield, ok? It's Athena's!' Hermes said casually, and performed a funny flip in the air, and vanished.

Great! As usual: a complete lack of information and extremely high levels of difficulty. Oh well...

I reluctantly poked the man on his shoulder. He was taken by surprise, but when he turned around and saw me, he was relieved:

'Oh! Hello buddy,' he whispered. 'Athena and Hermes mentioned that they would send someone out to help me. I can't go into much detail right now. All I want is to find out from the Three Grey Sisters where the Gorgons are...'

Grey Sisters and Gorgons...I was rather puzzled, but the man resumed his observation and remained alert. I had forgotten that he was a mortal like me. He couldn't read my thoughts! I poked him again softly.

'Oh! I do apologise, I don't mean to be rude. I am Perseus,' he whispered again, and pushed aside a few boughs in front of him, prompting me to take a look. In the midst of this darkness I managed to discern three ugly figures. They were dressed in black. Their faces were evil, pale and heavily wrinkled and - how creepy - they were completely eyeless too! But when I looked more carefully, I noticed that one of them was holding a single large eye. (Ewww!) She placed it on her forehead, looked around carefully and then passed it on to the next one. The second sister did exactly the same thing, and passed the eye on to the third. I realised that without the eye they were sharing, they would all three of them be blind.

'I must find a way to extract a very important piece of information from them: the Gorgons' lair!' Perseus hastened to say, 'I will explain later. It's a long story, and if their eye catches me, I am in big trouble!'

I pondered the situation for a little while, and then said:

'The fact that they are sharing one eye amongst themselves is their

weakness. If I manage to distract them, maybe you can snatch it from them.'

'Great idea, buddy. I will do my best.'

I swiped my finger to grab a stone, and threw it towards the Granny on the right.

'Someone is here!' she cried in her creepy voice. 'Sister, pass me the eye quickly! I need to see! We can eat mortal meat today,' she chortled.

The middle Granny snapped the eye out of her forehead, and handed it over. As soon as the Granny on the right placed it on her forehead, I grabbed a second stone and threw it towards the opposite side.

'No, no, here!' the Granny on the left exclaimed. 'Quickly! Pass me the eye!'

The moment the right Granny attempted to pass the eye to the left one, I took the chance and called Perseus:

'Now!'

He jumped from his hiding place like a deer. He performed an impressive leap, and snatched the eye from the hand of the Witch. In my world, Perseus would be a great goal-keeper!

All Three Grey Sisters were now blind. They started screaming and threatening the artful "thief". But without being able to see him, they were helpless.

'I am not here to harm you. All I want is to find out where the three Gorgons are. If you tell me, I promise I will give you your eye back,' Perseus said bravely.

After a while, the Grannies were forced to give him the information he wanted. The young man kept his promise. He was about to return the eye when I stopped him. His courage and his honesty were remarkable, but still, he was a mortal.

'Perseus, make sure you step far away, and I will give it back to them instead,' I said.

I "held" the disgusting eye with my finger (again, ewww!) and when I made sure Perseus was far away, I "placed" it back on the hands of one of the three Grey Sisters.

I didn't want to stay around and listen to their cursing shrill, so I followed Perseus' steps. Shortly after, the setting changed completely. The dark muddy wetlands gave way to a gorgeous landscape with bright sunlight and thick greenery. Perseus sat down for a break under a well-shaded spot, and narrated to me his amazing story: the story of a hapless mortal, whose father was the king of all gods...

Perseus's grandfather, the king of a powerful city called Argos, had received an ominous prophecy: the son of his daughter, beautiful Danae, would kill him. The fearful king locked the princess in an underground bronze chamber so that no one could reach her. But Zeus was charmed by Danae. Disguised as a shower of gold he sneaked into the bronze chamber and left her with child... (Gods do have great imagination indeed!) Perseus was born. Danae tried to hide him away for as long as she could. But eventually, the king became aware of the baby and became furious. He locked them both in a wooden chest and cast them into the sea.

But, thanks to Zeus, the chest washed up on the island of Seriphos. There, they were found by a nice man, Dictys. Perseus came of age safely. But Dictys's evil brother, Polydectes, who was also the king of the island, fell in love with Danae. In order to get rid of Perseus, he asked him to prove his bravery.

'You see, that was an insult. I wanted to become a hero and I took the challenge without thinking twice,' Perseus sighed. 'So I was assigned with killing a very powerful monster, Medusa. Out of the three mighty sisters, the Gorgons, she is the only mortal. These are human-shaped, hideous monsters, with large golden wings, massive bronze hands and pointy steel nails. In place of hair, they have venomous snakes. Their teeth are as sharp as knives. Their serpentine bodies are covered with thick scales. But the worst of all is that whoever looks upon their eyes is immediately turned to stone. I have already travelled to the other end of the world, but at least I now know where to find them: on an island far away, in the land of Night and Death.

After this, what I truly wanted to say was: 'Very nice to meet you, Perseus, but I really have to dash away!' I was too embarrassed though, and so gave it a little more thought. I mean, come on! My hero was under the cloak of two gods!

'Now what?' I asked him, pretending to be calm.

'Well. Right now we are on the realm beyond the North Wind. This is a blissful fairy-land with extremely happy people, the Hyperboreans, who live to an extreme age. Hermes and Athena told me that I will find extra help around here,' Perseus said with some hope in his eyes.

Indeed, I could already hear the sound of music and laughter approaching. A bunch of very good-looking, graceful and glowing people gathered around Perseus and started "bombarding" him with hospitality. Slightly embarrassed, he introduced himself politely and announced who had sent him there. The Hyperboreans lifted him up and placed him on a comfortable seat. They gave him a feast to eat and drink like a

king. Then they resumed their singing. A group of gorgeous young girls dragged him into a dance.

'Hey, hero! We have work to do!' I poked him. I was a bit annoyed.

Perseus immediately apologised to the people: he had to leave and he needed their help. The Hyperboreans brought three small gadgets and placed them in his hands. Honestly, I was jealous: a pair of winged Hermes-style sandals, a magic pouch that would safely take in anything (regardless of its size) and - most importantly - a cap (an import from the Underworld according to the fairy-people) that made the wearer invisible.

Seriously? It's not very difficult to become a hero with all these things, I thought. But, again, I felt embarrassed. Poor guy. Let's be honest, he had been through so much...

Perseus strapped on the sandals happily, he grabbed the cap and the pouch on his shoulder and took off. Literally and metaphorically! He felt like a child! Fair enough, it must be amazing to suddenly be able to fly...In the beginning, he of course made my head spin, but in the end he got used to it and, like a "second" Hermes, he easily flew towards the land where, according to the Witches, the Gorgons lived.

Thanks to these sandals, he flew across the ocean very quickly until we finally saw from afar the island of the Gorgons. When we came as close as we could in order recognise them, I prompted Perseus to stop.

'All right buddy, nothing to worry about. I will now put my magic cap on and the Gorgons will not see me,' Perseus said.

'Sure, but you will see them,' I said and reminded him that if he looked upon them, he would turn to stone.

Perseus landed on a rock. He was baffled. He thought he didn't have enough weapons to overwhelm these monsters. I placed Athena's shiny shield and Hermes's sword in his hands. Perseus cheered up a little but we both realised that a few problems remained unsolved.

'Ok,' I said, 'let's sum up: we have the winged sandals, the magic cap that makes you invisible, a defensive shield, a sword that can cut off Medusa's head and a pouch we can use to carry it...'

'I will hide behind the shield so that I don't look upon her and turn to stone, and you will guide my hand when I am holding the sword. You are not part of this world really, so you will not be petrified,' Perseus thought out loud.

'That won't be easy because you will be invisible!' I replied and we both put our thinking caps back on again. It can't be! Athena and Hermes must have predicted these hurdles. They must have made sure that the mortal hero had everything he needed with him for this difficult challenge. All he had to do was 'choose to use his mind' as the wise goddess had pointed out. We were missing something...

'Look, buddy! Athena's copper shield is so polished! Like a mirror...' Perseus suddenly noticed. 'Maybe, if Medusa faces her very own reflection she will turn to stone herself!'

'That's it Perseus! What an amazing observation!' I gasped. 'But we can't risk it. These sisters are obviously looking at each other without turning to stone...'

Perseus seemed puzzled.

'Why is it such a great idea then?'

'Because you can use the shield as a mirror! On its shiny surface you will be able to see Medusa's reflection and you can behead her without looking upon her!' I exclaimed.

Perseus was very excited. He stood up quickly, put the cap on, grabbed the shield and the sword, and took off.

After practis-
ing flying

"in reverse" for a little while, he flew backwards, straight towards the island, looking through the shield for the correct direction.

We were extremely lucky: when we approached, we noticed that the three monsters were all sleeping deeply. The snakes on their heads were also asleep. They were all hide-ous. I could see why a single gaze at them would petrify you!

Hopefully Perseus would succeed in slaying the mortal Gorgon without trying twice. I don't even want to imagine what would happen if one of them woke up before him killing Medusa! He only had one chance.

I held my breath when I saw this. One pouch, two winged sandals, a shield and a sword were actually sneaking up above Medusa...

The shield caught the sunlight and shone like light-ning into Medusa's eyes and awoke her, but the sword was already swinging through the air and....whoosh! Medusa's head fell to the ground. The gruesome thud woke the snakes on the heads of the other two Gor-gons. At once they let out their horrific hiss and awoke the two sisters. The two IMMORTAL sisters!

'Perseus! Quick! You must leave now!' I ex-claimed anxiously.

'The head! You must pick up the head! I can't leave the sword behind! Nor the shield!' Perseus cried as anxiously as I did.

I nervously grabbed the flying pouch with one finger and swiped the horrible head into it. I was rather disgusted, but Per-seus took off high with a spectac-ular flight, fixing his sword through his belt with one hand, and snatching the pouch from my finger without even abandoning the shield. In the meantime, the two immortal Gorgons had also started running after him frantically. It looked like Perseus was spinning around, because the pouch, the wings, the shield and the sword were all moving around very awkwardly. As a result, the Gorgons didn't really know where to target. Perseus kept on climbing in the air. In the end, the Gorgons had to give up and fly back to their island in distress. Danger had passed, and Perseus had proven how truly brave he was.

But on our way out of this island, we noticed something strange. A fabulous, white winged-horse sprang from Medusa's severed neck. Taken aback, Perseus took off his cap, and stood still in the air in complete bewilderment. We both stared at the horse flying towards the horizon. We looked at each other mouths agape, and burst into laughter at the same time.

'I think we have seen pretty much everything by now, haven't we?' Perseus said cheerily.

'Well, let's not tempt fate! Besides, don't forget you are the child of... golden rain!' I said and we both burst into laughter again.

'Hey buddy, I would like to thank you a million times,' Perseus turned serious. 'I wouldn't have made it without you...'

'I should thank you for giving me the chance to share such an adventure with a real hero,' I replied. I really meant it.

I remembered something I had heard before: 'the value of our friends reflects our own value.' Just like a polished shield...

PERSEUS, THE BEAUTY AND THE BEAST

Perseus began the journey of return to Seriphos.

'I am worried about my mum, buddy,' he confessed. 'This Polydectes is very sneaky. I am sure he will take advantage of my absence to put pressure on her. Unfortunately, in my world, women are believed to be weak.'

I reminded him that Danae could rely on Dictys, the king's kind brother and so he calmed down a little.

We were taking the time to enjoy our flight over the calm ocean. I was wondering why I was still with this hero since I had already helped him kill Medusa? Could it be that there were more adventures coming ahead?

'We will now cross over the kingdom of the Aithiopians,' Perseus said cheerfully.

Right. As if I even knew this place. I didn't have a clue. I was already awful at real geography (my school-marks are terrible) let alone mythological geography!

We were now flying over a long rocky coast. On the horizon you could almost see some houses and palaces in the distance.

As Perseus was flying high over the coastline, something caught my eye. I zoomed in, and was surprised to see the figure of a woman. Yes! A beautiful young woman was chained to the rocks! What was this about? Obviously, a woman in a weak position!

'Perseus! Look! Over there! Do you see that young woman over those rocks?'

The hero flew hurriedly towards the spot I pointed out. The woman's desperate screaming reached our ears. We came across an admittedly beautiful but also terrified captive. The girl who was screaming the place down a few seconds earlier turned speechless at the sight of the strong hero with the winged sandals! And as for Perseus...I had to use my finger in order to close his mouth. I guess this must be what people call "love at first sight". Oh dear! Boring...

'Hey! You guys! Come on! A girl being chained to a sea-cliff doesn't look good!' I told them firmly.

Startled, they both smiled bashfully. The young woman seemed once again very scared, and began telling us her bitter story at full speed. Perseus was listening as if he was petrified in front of Medusa! Poor hero! What a pity!

To cut a long story short this is what we found out: this girl was princess Andromeda, the daughter of the king of the Aithiopians. Her mother did something really naive by boasting that Andromeda was more beautiful than the nymphs, the daughters of Nereus, who was a sea-god. Nereus, in order to punish her for her arrogance, sent out an enormous sea-dragon which was devouring the Aithiopians in droves! The king asked the oracle for a prophecy. It told him that in order to rid his kingdom of this disaster, his precious daughter must be sacrificed to the monster. So there she is. The princess is "served" and ready to eat! So basically, she is paying for the mistake of her parents!

'Don't worry Andromeda. I will be your saviour,' love-struck Perseus hastened to say while the girl looked at him lustfully. I wanted to tell him that using "we" would be a bit more polite but I didn't have a chance! Something disturbed the sea ominously. The scaly curves of an unknown sea-snake whipped the sea surface into foam. Petrified, we saw the head of a gigantic sea dragon emerging through the foam, roaring terribly. Every single trace of romance was wiped out by the salivating monster's smelly fish-like breath and its large sharp teeth!

Perseus, shield and sword in hand, stood courageously in front of the girl. I tried to break the chains of Andromeda but in vain. I needed a tool. Suddenly, I remembered that Hermes's sword could thrust into anything.

'Perseus, you must break the girl's chains with the sword of Hermes,' I said.

But he had no time to react. The snake was now dangerously close to them, and Perseus had to protect Andromeda without leaving her exposed to the monster. The dragon rose up, and stretched its head, ready to attack. Perseus sprang towards it, and managed to thrust his sword into the dragon. But for the sea-monster, this felt like a scratch! The blow annoyed the beast; it swirled around, and by turning an impressive somersault in the air, it collapsed into the sea. The monster's fall caused large waves that crashed against the steep rocks, soaking the unfortunate couple. From the violent thrash, the rocks around them filled with all kinds of writhing fish. If it wasn't for this dragon, I thought, this glut of fish could feed a great deal of people!

'Quick, my friend, you must distract him with something! If you hold him off, I will have more time to free Andromeda,' exclaimed Perseus.

Suddenly I saw the head of the sea-snake rising up from the water once again. It now looked even more ferocious than before. It opened its mouth wide and...without thinking too much

about it, I used my finger to grab a large fish from the rocks, and threw it in. The snake didn't expect that. This delicious mouthful distracted it perfectly. It paused, and chomped on it with pleasure. That's it! I was now feverishly collecting fish from the rocks in order to feed the mouth of the beast! I have to say: in the past I had the chance to feed several little animals, but never a giant sea-dragon!

Perseus seized the opportunity at once. He turned around quickly and wielded the divine sword against the iron chains that bound Andromeda to the rocks. The blade sliced through the metal as if it were butter. Perseus didn't miss the opportunity to take the girl in his arms (of course!) and hid her in a narrow slot between the rocks. The sea-dragon wouldn't be able to fit through there. Within seconds, and whilst I was busy feeding the snake with a large fish, he took off and flew behind it. The sea-dragon, so caught into seafood-nibbling, didn't notice a thing. Perseus wrapped his legs behind its neck and used all his strength to plunge the sword into the beast's head. The sea-monster stood there motionless for a little while until it finally slumped into the sea causing massive waves. Perseus managed to fly away just before the snake disappeared under the water. The tumultuous sea turned red and the creature's writhing soon stopped.

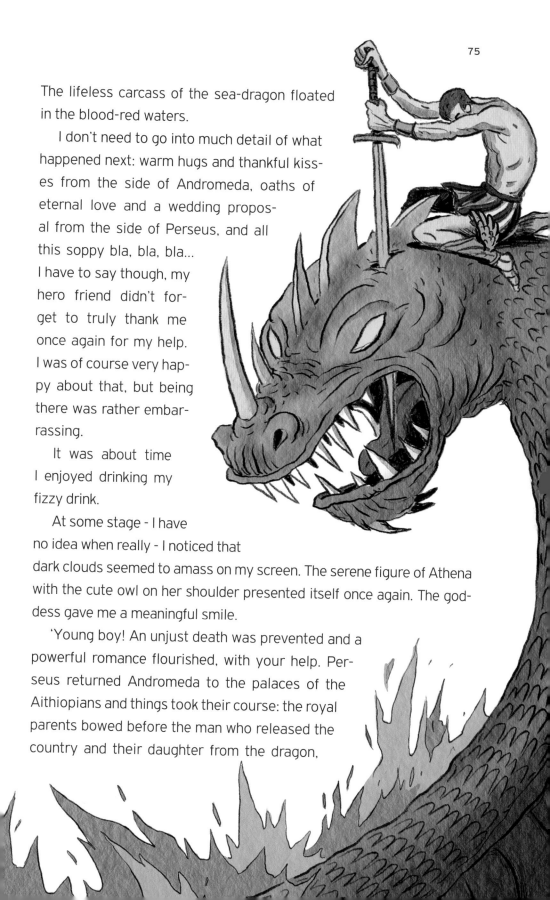

The lifeless carcass of the sea-dragon floated in the blood-red waters.

I don't need to go into much detail of what happened next: warm hugs and thankful kisses from the side of Andromeda, oaths of eternal love and a wedding proposal from the side of Perseus, and all this soppy bla, bla, bla... I have to say though, my hero friend didn't forget to truly thank me once again for my help. I was of course very happy about that, but being there was rather embarrassing.

It was about time I enjoyed drinking my fizzy drink.

At some stage - I have no idea when really - I noticed that dark clouds seemed to amass on my screen. The serene figure of Athena with the cute owl on her shoulder presented itself once again. The goddess gave me a meaningful smile.

'Young boy! An unjust death was prevented and a powerful romance flourished, with your help. Perseus returned Andromeda to the palaces of the Aithiopians and things took their course: the royal parents bowed before the man who released the country and their daughter from the dragon, and gave their permission for their marriage wholeheartedly. As far as Cassiopeia is concerned, Andromeda's mother, I think she learned her lesson: mortals must not boast or compare themselves with us gods. What they can do, is come to us and ask for our help, just like Perseus did. For this reason, the persecuted can always flee into our temples for refuge.' Her owl turned around and winked at me, or perhaps that was my imagination.

The goddess vanished in the clouds once again.

A small backstreet of an island appeared on the screen. A stooped beggar was sitting on a corner. He was hiding his face with his cloak. I heard him saying something really quietly. His voice sounded familiar:

'Thank gods you didn't go to the wedding of Perseus. You would have been bored...,' the beggar looked like he was talking to himself. 'Not to mention the food menu. It was seafood all the way! I suspect you are not looking forward to any type of fish in the near future, are you?'....

The beggar threw off his hood...and there he was! The golden locks of Hermes!

I didn't have the chance to say anything really, because the street was suddenly filled with angry men who were looking around for something.

'Did you see this?' Hermes said when they left. 'The minions of Polydectes are looking for the mother of Perseus! We are on Seriphos. Kind Dictys passed away, and poor Danae was left helpless. Instead of getting married against her will and honour, she chose to run away and hide. I think, my mortal friend, that Perseus needs your help urgently! I mean until he arrives here at least...' Hermes said, and then rolled his cape around himself and vanished.

Wait a minute. I didn't even know what Danae looked like! How would I find her? And even if I did, how would I be able to help her?

I didn't have time to finish my thoughts: the head of a beautiful woman popped very cautiously out of a large jar, right next to the spot where Hermes was sitting. She looked around in dismay. Perseus's resemblance to her was extraordinary.

'Ms Danae?' I said reluctantly, 'I am a friend of your son, Perseus'.

The woman looked at me in surprise.

'Of Perseus? My son?' she asked nervously. 'Is he ok? Do you know where he is?'

'He is just fine!' I reassured her. 'He has achieved great feats and he has also married the princess of the Aithiopians!'

Tears of happiness welled up in her eyes but then fear darkened them once again.

'Do you know, my boy,....is he going to come back here?' she asked eagerly.

'I am not sure,' I answered back gently, 'but I think that he will come to find you as soon as possible because he was really worried about you.'

'I hope he will find me soon enough...' she exclaimed with a tone that scared me.

'Can I perhaps help you until he is back?' I asked.

'Oh thank you my dear, but I am not sure what you can do...I am desperately looking for a place where this evil man, king Polydectes, will not be able to harm me...'

Athena's words flashed into my mind!

'Ms Danae! No one can hurt you inside the temple! All the persecuted can flee there for refuge!' I told her full of excitement.

'That's it! You're right! But...how will I make it there? Polydectes has released all kinds of lapdogs on the streets to search for me. How will I get away from them?'

I thought about this very carefully and...Could I do this? I could give it a shot.

I zoomed out a little. Danae got smaller at once. I could now see all the streets around her.

'Ms Danae, do you know where the temple is?' I asked hurriedly. A few men were dashing down a narrow passage just nearby.

The woman nodded her head 'yes' and looked behind anxiously. These men were already turning into the street where she was. I quickly tipped over a cart with my finger to block it off.

'Run to the temple, Ms Danae! I will hold them off!' I exclaimed. This felt like a proper video game. I had to surmount all these obstacles, and help her cross the town and slip away from the men who were after her. The king's minions were trying to block every single access to the temple but, thanks to my intervention, she picked her way through each time. I was leading the way by setting up barriers, opening up new exit routes and by building "staircases" and passages... I never thought that helping the mother of a friend - who also happens to be a digital and a mythological hero - would be so much fun! (Crazy, eh?)

At last, Danae reached the temple. The men of Polydectes were dangerously close. But the priestesses saw this horrified and out-of-breath woman, and quickly took her inside the sacred place. Danae entered the building and finally took some rest by sitting next to the altar. These men couldn't hurt her in any way anymore. As long as she was there, she was protected by the gods and no one would dare lay a finger on her. Danae's chasers were now unable to do anything and so they left to inform the king.

Not long after, Perseus and Andromeda entered the temple. Danae fell into her son's arms. The moment the hero had arrived in town he was approached by a "beggar" who told him about Dictys and his mother's struggle to reach the temple.

After introducing Andromeda to Danae, Perseus pulled off the winged sandals and took the cap of Hades, and together with the shield of Athena and the sword of Hermes, he placed them on the altar with great respect. These were suddenly veiled by a white cloud and then vanished.

'I know you must be fed up with me thanking you non-

stop, buddy, but I can't tell you how grateful I am,' Perseus said warmly. He then turned to the two women and announced:

'You two wait here. Polydectes and I have unfinished business...'

I "followed" him to the palaces. Holding the pouch with Medusa's head, the hero entered the royal hall. Polydectes was in there, along with all his courtiers and fawners. The king turned pale at the sight before him. Obviously, he wasn't expecting to see him alive again.

'I did what you asked, my king,' he said calmly.

The king's subordinates started hurling insults at him. Polydectes plucked up his courage and mocked him:

'I bet you didn't manage to slay Medusa!' Everyone broke into rude scornful laughter.

'Since you don't trust my word, you must see proof, my king,' Perseus answered back. Then he took the head of the dead monster out of his pouch and held it up whilst looking away.

The king and his men turned to stone at once and the throne room was now filled with lifeless statues. Mocking, ridiculous expressions had been captured on their frozen faces. It was a terrifying scene to behold. But then, something unexpected happened: a little owl came through the window, swooped over the statue of Polydectes and pooped on his head! The pouch and Medusa's head vanished into a cloud whilst the voice of the wise goddess echoed inside the hall:

'Perseus, you deserve the favour of gods and humans. You can now peacefully enjoy the rewards of courage. I will keep Medusa's head and I will use it to decorate my unbreakable shield. Like Polydectes, everyone who looks upon it, will receive the price of disrespect.'

The little owl went to perch on my friend's shoulder. I wouldn't wait this time. I winked at it first!

THE LABYRINTH
AND THE LITTLE-THUMB TRICK

And then? Darkness. Total darkness. Pitch-black. Did my tablet break down again? Or did it go back to normal perhaps? I turned it on and off again. Nothing. But this time, I think I could hear the sound of splashing waves, and something like...Yes. I could actually hear muffled mourning blended in with some talking...What was this about? I scrolled down, and...how bizarre! This black was not darkness. It was actually something. A black cloth! No, not laundry. It was a black sail! I zoomed out, and an ancient Greek wooden boat was revealed sailing on my screen. Apart from the strong rowers, I also noticed many young men and women on its deck. This quiet mourning was coming from them. They were weeping in the arms of the men, it seemed. Another unusual adventure! Maybe I was coming late for this one, don't you think? Could this mourning be the result of a bad ending? An impressive looking young man with blonde, all curly, shoulder-length hair was proudly standing at its stern. He seemed different from all the rest. It wasn't just about his imposing form giving away his great physical strength; he was also of noble appearance and his expression was shining with confidence and composure. He smiled warmly when he saw me, as if he was expecting me:

'Tim! My friend! Welcome on board! Bright Apollo did warn me that I was going to meet you, when I sacrificed a wild bull in his honour - just before we set sail for Athens. I am Theseus! You will hear many people say how great a hero I am, having completed all these difficult feats. But I prefer to introduce myself as the son of Aegeus, who is now the king of Athens.' With a playful tone of voice, the imposing young man added: 'The truth is, however, that adventures draw me in like magnets!'

That's something I actually share with this Theseus! I would love to hear all about his feats, but I was very curious about these mourning women.

'Hello to you, Theseus!' I returned his greeting. 'What is the matter here? These girls on your boat, they don't seem very excited about the cruis...ehm, the trip!'

His face darkened:

'How could they be, my friend? We are all like lambs to the slaughter! Horrific death awaits us at the end of this journey!'

I couldn't understand a thing. Theseus laughed when he realised how confused I was:

'I will explain right away: many years ago, youths from all over Greece participated in these great athletic games that took place in Athens. One of these youths, Androgeos, son of the king of Crete, Minos, took all the prizes and was crowned victor. He wanted to win all competitions and my father made a terrible mistake by taking him to this dangerous hunting expedition. Androgeos was killed while trying to kill a wild bull. King Minos never forgave my father; he had exposed Androgeos to danger whilst he was his own guest. So the king used his army to besiege Athens, and in order to forsake the city he forced my father to pay an overwhelming blood tax: every year, seven young men and seven young women are sent to Crete. There, in a dark maze, the labyrinth, they are devoured by a monster, called the Minotaur. This is a wild creature with the head of a bull and the body of a man. It feeds off flesh. Young men and women have been dying this horrible death for years now...'

'How about you, Theseus? What is your part in all this?' I asked curiously.

'I was not here when this disaster happened, Tim. I was raised in the town of my mother, Aethra. I have just come of age, so I came to Athens to meet my father. This is how I found out about this blood-soaked "tax". I believe that all these youths have been wasted in the sunless Labyrinth as retribution to Androgeos's recklessness. I made it clear to my father that I can't stay indifferent towards my city's on-going suffering. I wish to confront the monster and slay it. Athenians will then no longer weep over their children.'

I couldn't help but admire the boldness and the kind heart of Theseus. He was truly determined.

'And how do you plan to make this happen, Theseus?' I asked.

'My heart is brave and my arms are strong. But I also know that for the gods these are not good enough...Your presence here is proof of that! Apollo also told me that, when necessary, goddess Aphrodite will also be by my side. Let us reach Crete safe and sound, and then we'll see what we can do!' said Theseus. To me, it seemed that he was more impatient rather than anxious about it.

'And the black sail...' I asked curiously, 'is this some kind of custom?''

'We are hoisting a black sail as a sign of grief after the tax we are paying,' explained Theseus. 'I promised my father however, that if we make it through, I will change it to white. He will be so happy when he sees it from afar!'

The wooden trireme flew across the deep-blue waters and the wind blew against the square black sail. Theseus's companions seemed a little calmer now. His attitude was rather surprising: he was the son of a king, and yet he was addressing everyone in a simple and polite manner. There was still time, before reaching the shores of Crete, to ask Theseus more about his past adventures.

'When I left Troezen - that is the town in south Greece where I grew up in - my mother begged me to travel to Athens by boat. You see, the actual road was full of dangerous bandits and robbers. But, as you can imagine, I was boiling inside, so I went overland. Well! I didn't regret it! I have to say: I wasn't bored at all!' he exclaimed in high spirits.

He first narrated his encounter with giant Periphetes, who used an iron club to kill all the poor travellers who happened to be in his path. Theseus managed to crush him, and kept his club too.

'Look! Here it is!' he said, and opened a piece of cloth to show me the lethal weapon. Needless to say, I wouldn't have been able to even push it! If he was that strong, I thought, surely he could also defeat the Minotaur...

'Then,' went on Theseus, 'and whilst walking through an extremely narrow path along a cliff's edge, I came across a savage man named Sciron. He was known for forcing passers-by to wash his feet. When they did, he kicked them over the cliff into the sea. So I decided to encounter him and...'

'Let me guess!' I interrupted him. 'It looked like Sciron wasn't able to fly after all!' I said and we both burst into laughter. But the laughter drained from our faces when we noticed that the water was foaming up on a spot somewhere near the boat. Luckily it was just a shoal of glowing flying fish. They were beating their iridescent wings, gliding over the

sea and diving back into the water with remarkable grace. Truly unique animals! A fish and a bird in one!

'Indeed, Tim, the kingdom of Poseidon is full of wonderful creatures!' Theseus agreed with me and continued narrating his exciting stories.

'While I was approaching the Isthmus of Corinth, I came across a notorious bandit named Sinis. His strength was beastly. He used to bend two enormous pine trees down to the ground, and tie up his victims to their edges. When he let the trees go, the victims were torn apart. But in the end, he was also defeated in the very same way that he killed his own victims...Later, when I reached the banks of Cephissus River, just outside Athens, I encountered another nasty bandit: Procrustes. He was rather professional about it! He tied his unfortunate victims up to a bed he had built. If their legs were shorter than the length of the bed, he stretched them on the rack. If their legs were longer, he chopped them off! Well. This bed became his deathbed in the end! I was so happy that this land had been cleared of this vermin. Travellers can now pass by securely!' said Theseus, whilst I was thinking that many modern horror films were not even ready for these types of scenes! Theseus deserved the title of the hero beyond any doubt.

'We are almost there!' he shouted, pointing the land on the horizon. The crew was nervous about it, but Theseus was trying to encourage everyone.

'Look! Even Poseidon is on our side!' he exclaimed in high spirits, and pointed to the water right next to the stern, where a flock of cute dolphins were swimming along with the boat.

But suddenly, the image of one of the dolphins "froze" into a painting. I zoomed out and I realised that the dolphin was part of a beautiful wall-painting, a fresco. I was inside an impressive palace. The multi-storey complex was supported by wide dark-red columns. The walls were all wonderfully painted with vivid colours, with themes inspired by the natural world of the Mediterranean: birds, flowers, animals, even dolphins and flying fish! But one of these frescoes caught my attention the most. I thought it depicted a rare sport or something. Three human figures, two women and one man, were performing acrobatic leaps over a huge charging bull, which was dominating the centre of the painting. By grasping the bull by its horns they flipped over its back!

So this must have been the palace of Minos in Knossos, on the island of Crete. I heard some talking in the background. It was coming from one of the halls inside the palace. I followed the source of the echo and I ended up in a magnificent room, where Theseus and his companions were now gathered. The Athenians were surrounded by people who, unlike them, they were not wearing chitons. Their clothing was different and very unique. They were definitely Minoans. The men had long black hair and wore short skirts with tight belts that held their waists in. But Minoan women looked even more impressive: their dark wavy hair was hanging down over their breasts, which were left exposed by their tight short-sleeved blouses! Their long dresses flared out from their narrow waists into rows of ruffles that emphasized their elegant curves. Their eyes and their lips were adorned with makeup and they wore dazzling jewellery. They were all magnificent, carrying with them an air of confidence. These particular women didn't seem weak! They must have been equal to men.

In the middle of the hall, the noble king Minos was sitting on his alabaster throne. The thirteen youths of Athens were trembling with fear. Theseus, however, was standing fearless in front of him, without even lowering his eyes. He was talking to the nobleman boldly, explaining who he was. Minos was impressed by this man's bravery, but also by his eyes which remained stern and cold.

'I am glad Aegeus kept his promise this year too. You are welcome to be our houseguests for now, but tonight you will be taken to the

Labyrinth. The Minotaur will be honoured to "dine" on the prince of Athens...' he smiled scornfully, and signalled to his guards to show the fourteen youths out. Wow! King Minos had it coming!

While the youths were making their way out, a beautiful young girl appeared amongst the rest of the Minoan women. Theseus picked her out and gave her an admiring glance. The scene was followed by the sound of muffled giggling. I bet this was Aphrodite! Then, I saw a beautiful small winged boy; like an illusion really. He was pointing his arrows towards the girl. One of these invisible arrows pierced her heart, and then the boy disappeared! As soon as that happened, the girl returned his glance with a lustful look and a flushed cheeks. There we go again! Another soppy love story...It looks to me like goddess Aphrodite can play games with the hearts of the mortals like nothing...

Theseus and his companions were taken to a covered courtyard, where they were served a generous meal, water and wine. The seven poor young women could hardly touch it. This Minos had a very dark sense of humour indeed! Theseus reassured his companions and promised them that, when thrown into the maze, he would step forward. But he seemed worried himself. He looked at me, moved slightly to the side, and said:

'Tim, I have to admit that this Labyrinth is a problem. I have heard that its design has no parallel. It is an architectural wonder. Its complexity is so incredible - corridor branching off corridor - that, once inside, it is impossible to escape it. No one has ever made it...'

At that moment, the love-struck, attractive woman came out of a dark corner. She was holding a ball of thread. She came close to Theseus and hurriedly said:

'Brave Theseus, I am Ariadne, the daughter of Minos. I told my father I will be fetching some wool for weaving from the storerooms, but in actual fact I wanted to meet you. I am very upset with the thought of you being devoured by the Minotaur. I am desperate to help you save your lives, but I don't know how!' she sighed.

I thought: 'GPS is exactly what you need.' But that would be an odd luxury in this "space-time". Whilst Theseus and Ariadne were making eyes at each other, I was trying hard to come up with a solution. How could someone walk through an unknown path and then find their way back again? One must somehow mark their route. I remembered the fairy tale of Little Thumb: always leave behind a trail that cannot be erased...That's it!

'Ariadne, the solution lies in your hands!' I exclaimed with excitement and pointed to the ball of thread that the princess was holding. The young couple looked at each other in bewilderment.

'Theseus, think! While you will be walking through the Labyrinth, you can slowly start unwinding that piece of thread. When you hopefully defeat the Minotaur, you can roll it back, by following the route you took in the first place!' I said. I was so happy.

Theseus bowed before me in respect.

'Tim, Apollo's decision to send you here was not random. Thank you, my friend. You are truly smart!' he said, and I burst with pride!

At that moment, the guards came in to take the Athenians. Ariadne was in tears. She promised that she would wait for Theseus until he returned from the Labyrinth. She then disappeared inside the halls of the palace.

The moment of truth had come.

The guards led the fourteen youths to the entrance of the Labyrinth, where a pair of torches were burning, their light too weak to illuminate this thick, intimidating darkness.

Just like he'd promised, Theseus stepped forward, keeping the ball of thread well-hidden. Just a couple of steps later, he turned around and signalled to everyone to stay put. He then advanced forwards, holding a torch. The Labyrinth was exactly as he had described. New passages were constantly opening up in front of him. His back was concealed under the thick darkness, but the thread that was to save his life was already unrolling behind him. Suddenly, Theseus stopped. A menacing roar was heard from the depths of the maze, causing the Labyrinth to shake. Without losing heart, the hero headed towards the roar.

Ahead, his torch illuminated the figure of a horrific monster, whose body was blocking the whole passage. The Minotaur's big bulky head was there, foaming at the mouth and breathing a furious breath. Broken bones and human skulls were scattered all around him. How creepy! The beast rushed with his big horns against Theseus. As agile as a panther, the hero dodged the lethal horns and grabbed Minotaur from his neck. The beast desperately tried to get away from the hands of Theseus, who was now strangling him tightly.

It only lasted for a few minutes. Once Theseus released his iron grip, the Minotaur dropped to the ground, breathless. It was my turn to bow before this brave hero. He made it once again! He looked happy. He rolled back the thread and walked back to the entrance of the Labyrinth. There, the thirteen Athenians, along with Ariadne, were anxiously wait-

ing for him. Luckily, the guards of Minos, certain of the youths' death, had already gone much earlier. As soon as Theseus appeared through the Labyrinth opening, everyone erupted in enthusiastic cheers. The Athenians were safe!

Through hidden passages, in the midst of the night, Ariadne led them out of the palace and the city. Not long after, the youths reached the harbour. All fourteen of them, plus the young princess, went aboard the Athenian trireme where the crew was already waiting with great patience following Theseus's orders. They had to set sail very quickly before being discovered.

Otherwise, the Minoans would chase them. Theseus had told me that these island people were the most competent navigators in the whole of the Mediterranean.

That was when I came up with a new idea.

'This club you showed me before, can you use it?' I asked the hero.

'I wouldn't carry it all the way here if I couldn't!' he answered full of cheer.

'Then, maybe we can secure a great advantage against the Minoans in case they come after us with their ships...' I said and I explained my idea.

'Great plan!' said Theseus and got down to work. With his club, he broke the wooden ships of the Minoans and in a few minutes they were full of holes! They were so damaged, they wouldn't get far!

Theseus and his companions set sail for Athens just before sunset. The deck was bustling with joy and laughter, but soon, this beautiful scene disappeared from the screen. I could still see the blue of the sea, but only from above. I scrolled the scene to the right. There, a middle-aged noble-looking man was waiting at the edge of a cliff, overlooking the horizon. I realised that he could not see me.

'It can't be; they will show up soon! Oh, Theseus, my boy! If I never see you again, I will die! I will throw myself off the cliff and find some peace...' I heard him saying anxiously.

Dear me! This was Aegeus...The sail! Did they remember to change their sail? I looked carefully into the horizon and saw a black dot. Oh, no! That's not fair! This adventure doesn't deserve a bad ending.

'I am sorry, Tim, but this is how the Aegean Sea was named: the king saw the black sail that Theseus forgot to change, and his pain was so great, he flung himself off the cliff into the sea...' Apollo's voice was heard saying.

'Don't I deserve a tiny little bit of help?' I begged him in the sweetest way possible.

'What's on your mind?' he asked reluctantly.

'You know...this flash-trick you have used...If you try it on Aegeus for a little while, I will have some more time!'

So while Aegeus was trying to pick out the ship on the horizon, he was dazzled by a sudden flash. He shut his eyes and stepped back.

As quickly as I could, I "ran" my finger on the screen to quickly reach the trireme of Theseus. Would I make it?

'The sail, Theseus, the sail! Change the sail!' I started screaming as soon as I saw the ship.

The people in the café were looking at me strangely. I "sank" in my seat rather embarrassed and anxiously approached the ship. Theseus was already shouting out at the crew to drop the black sail.

As soon as I got close enough, I carefully said to him:

'Theseus, please don't ask why, but you must name this sea the "Aegean", in honour of your father who loves you so much. And when you finally meet, please don't forget to pay your special respects to god Apollo...'

Theseus, full of joy, nodded positively and waved me off warmly with both his arms. A big "thank you" travelled over the waves.

I quickly "ran" back to the edge of the cliff. Aegeus was still rubbing his eyes. Phew...Thank heavens, binoculars and sunglasses didn't exist in his world! The king resumed his search on the horizon. The screen then slowly started turning black, and before switching completely "off" again, I heard him screaming:

'It's white! It's white!'

I leaned on the tablet and buried my face in my arms.

I needed a holiday from this holiday!

HERCULES TURNS
THE KING OF THE JUNGLE INTO A COAT!

I felt a light tap on my shoulder followed by a voice:

'Hey, buddy, are you ok?'

I jumped up. A guy with a wide smile - probably a tourist - was standing over me.

'Ah, yes...yes! I am fine!' I replied.

'I heard you screaming and I was worried...'

'No...! You see, I am playing this game. I got a little overexcited...' (How embarrassing!)

'All right, then,' he said politely and left by sneaking a glimpse at my tablet:

'Great screensaver! Have a nice day!'

I quickly turned to the screen. A proud eagle was sweeping circles against a mass of peach-gold clouds. Hmm...

'So, Tim. No more bravery?' said the eagle in Zeus's voice!

'I am Zeus, young mortal! Don't you know I can transform myself?'

I looked around. Luckily, no one was watching. I sighed and talked to the bird (!)

'Mr Zeus, I am glad to se...hear you again!' I said.

The king of the gods was transformed back into his regular form. He bellowed with laughter, but soon became serious, and said:

'So? Is that it? You can't have more adventures with us humble gods and super-heroes?'

'No, I do...!'

'Because I was about to introduce you to my son, the greatest of heroes of all,' he went on saying.

You think he meant...

'Well, of course!' he said, 'Everyone has heard of Hercules the great! He is the strongest of all men, but he is also a very kind and honest boy, although rather unlucky. He has been through a lot...'

I can't believe I had the chance to hang around with the greatest hero from the world of Greek mythology! How cool!

'My wife, Hera, could never forgive him for being the child I had with a mortal,' Zeus carried on. 'She has been running after him ever since he was born...'

There we go. Another child paying for the mistakes of his own parents!

Zeus gave me a firm look. He had already read my thought.

'I do apologise, Mr Zeus, but this is how I see things. It seems you can't keep your eyes off every single mortal woman!' I said, and waited for the thunderbolts.

But Zeus almost smirked under his proud beard.

'You are not afraid to express your opinion, mortal. I appreciate that. But you should not judge what is happening here according to the rules of your world...'

I remembered how Metis-prudence came to be "swallowed", and how wisdom was later born. Maybe he was right...

'However, some things are common in both worlds, Tim...' he added vaguely, and disappeared.

The clouds cleared, and the screen was now "flying" towards the ground. It felt like I was an eagle myself. The scene was constantly zooming in. I could see plains and mountains, until I finally "reached" a highland that looked familiar. Yes! This was the place where Apollo and I came once to slay the Python! But a beautiful ancient city, adorned with a spectacular temple, was now here. This was Delphi. So Apollo did establish his oracle here after all - with great success from what I could see. Loads of people were coming and going through the temple; they looked like ants, while the temple truly looked like the "navel of the world".

In the end, the picture on the screen "landed" on a spot right outside the temple: an almost giant, extremely strong man was standing out from all the rest. He was sitting on a marble step and he was leaning on an enormous wooden club that reminded

me of Hephaestus. He seemed absorbed and sceptical. He was wearing a lion's coat over his back; when alive, this must have definitely been the king of the jungle! The animal's injured head was covering half of the strong man's head, like a helmet. Under the lion's huge teeth, I could see his thick black messy hair all mixed with his shaggy brows. I have to say: I never thought that Hercules would look so...savage. He had nothing in common with the polished beauty of Theseus. But every inch of his muscular body was clearly screaming: DANGER, KEEP AWAY!

'Hercules?' I told him softly.

He seemed absent-minded:

'Hey, kid. You must be Tom, no?'

'Ehm, Tim...'

'That's right. Tim. I just received an oracle that I will meet you.'

He stared at me in bewilderment:

'Excuse me, I am really sorry, but I can't see how a child can help. Anyway, we have to respect the gods,' he compromised.

That's not a good start for a top super-hero. I hate being belittled. Anyway.

'Why did you consult the oracle?' I changed subject.

'It's a long and painful story I am afraid...Now, I am obliged to follow the prophecy: I must meet King Eurystheus in order to serve my sentence!' he said, and then jumped up as if he had remembered the oven was on. With his extra-large club, he started striding down the slope without paying me much attention.

Great. This hero doesn't engage much. I noticed that passers-by were surprised and amazed by his giant figure, but he behaved as if he didn't realise or as if he didn't care at all about the type of impression he was making. He lived in his own world, a world that was not going particularly well...

'Hercules! Wait!' I said while following him on the screen. 'If you don't explain to me, then I won't know what to do.'

Without stopping his descent and without giving me a single look, he said:

'Don't worry, Tom (!) I have to encounter dangerous threats, and I will do so on my own. It has been my fault and I have to be punished for it. We don't need to risk more people's lives for it. Besides, I am the strongest man on earth. Nothing scares me!'

Both deaf and stubborn: what a great combination for a hero!

He realised I was vexed because he looked at me out of the corner of his eye, and hastened to say:

'By Zeus - that is my own father - if I need your help, I will ask for it.'

Thank heavens the screen went black. My presence was unnecessary. This first encounter with famous Hercules ended up badly. Why would Zeus make me do this then? And what was it that Hercules did, and now had to be punished for? I have to say: I was really curious about this all.

Not long after, his figure filled the whole screen again. He was on a mountain and he was dripping with sweat. Time must have passed more quickly in his world, because the surroundings were completely different and he looked drained.

'Tom, I told you I will ask for your help if I need it. But there you are again!' he said with the innocent eyes of a small child.

'First of all, let's make this clear: my name is Tim!' I said firmly. 'So, are you finally going to tell me what is going on?'

'All right, kid, ehm..., Tim. I promise I will explain everything later. First, I must kill this frightful lion. Eurystheus has sent me here, in Nemea, to rid both animals and humans of this vicious threat that ravages their land. I spotted the lion and shot at it with all my arrows, but its skin is impervious to attack. I must strangle it to death with my own hands. I have been trying to catch it for days now. I have been tracking it in every single valley, plain and mountain...no luck yet. Whenever I am close, it slips out like a big cat. Maybe you can come up with something...'

I realised that he was all over the place. We wouldn't work this out unless he first killed this "vicious threat" he was going on about.

'Where is this lion now?' I asked.

'It likes to rest around here, in a cave. I tried to catch it, but it slipped out through the back entrance.'

'Does this mean that if you manage to trap it, you would be able to kill it?'

Instead of answering he let loose with a loud guffaw, showing me off the lion skin over his back, as if he was a fashion model!

'I have to admit though,' he became serious again, 'this lion was much smaller than the monster of Nemea, but when I killed it, I was only eighteen years old after all!'

I don't know how he did this: he was driving me up the wall, but at the same time he was rather exciting!

'So the answer to my question is yes, I guess,' I said firmly. 'This means that the problem comes down to how we are going to trap it.'

I thought that setting a trap would work. This cave could be the solution to our problem.

'Hercules, you just said that the cave has a back entrance. Do you think you could block it up with a few pieces of rock?'

His face brightened up:

'Great idea, Tim! This is what I should do! Then, I will trap the lion inside the cave and give it a lesson!' he exclaimed full of joy.

With a couple of strides, he reached the cave opening, and started collecting large pieces of rock - for him they were pebbles really! Imagine what he could do when he was not tired...Hercules piled up the rocks at the back entrance, and blocked up the whole opening. Then, he said:

'Now, I must find the lion and make it come in here!'

I remembered this trick I did with Danae, when I helped her reach the temple.

'I think I can tell you exactly where the lion is and then help you trap it into the cave,' I said.

For a while, he was reluctant, but then cracked a wide smile:

'Thank you, Tim! This will save me a lot of trouble!'

Indeed, I zoomed out so I could inspect the whole area. I "searched" around for the lion but in vain. Just when I had started turning desperate, I saw its tail hanging from a tree.

I helped Hercules reach the spot. When he got there, the lion jumped up and ran quickly. I started laying the route for him in order to block the way and force it into the cave. This chase was really fun! At least for me. I was just watching after all. I was like a race-car passenger. Hercules was striding all along, running fast like a deer. He managed two things with this: firstly, to drive the animal into the cave, and secondly, to wear it out. The lion's hair was now sparkling with sweat. The cool and quiet cave was nothing but heaven for the exhausted animal. Without thinking about it, it entered through its dark opening. That was it! Hercules rushed into the cave too, and blocked, with his own body, the only opening left. The cave was shaking with menacing growls. Instead of stepping back, the hero went forward, and disappeared into the dark opening. No matter how close I got, I couldn't clearly see clearly inside the cave - apart from for the lion's red eyes that were glowing like fire. The wild growl blended with some heavy grunting, then turned into roaring and screaming...I was worried. Hercules's strength and confidence were undeniable. But what if he had underestimated the enemy?

My anguish didn't last long. Everything went quiet shortly after, and the giant man came back to light, dragging out the breathless beast by its tail.

'Tim! That was it, my friend! I choked the blasted thing!' he panted, and leaned on the animal's massive carcass to take some rest. His body was covered in scratches and wounds, but he didn't seem to care much. Shortly after, he took a large knife out of his waistband, and started skinning the animal. I felt really sick myself, but for him it was a normal thing to do - just like a child carving a piece of wood. I tried to look away from this gross, and asked Hercules (again) for some answers.

The hero sighed deeply and began telling me his story:

'Hera was always causing me trouble; ever since I was born. I mean this. One night, she sent two large snakes to finish me off in my crib. Thank gods I woke up from the hissing sound, and strangled them.'

A baby strangling two large snakes with his bare hands! Unbelievable! Hercules didn't seem surprised by the stunned expression on my face and continued:

'Later, when I grew up, I married a kind princess who gave me three sons. But one night, Hera inflicted madness on me, and I lost my mind. When I came back to my senses, I saw my family lying dead all around; my hands were soaked in blood. How can someone live with this? I wanted to die and rid myself of this unbearable guilt...'

The hero paused, and hid his face in his hands. I was heartbroken. What a sad story! This goddess was so harsh.

'Hercules, I can't even imagine what this felt like, but I don't think you should carry the weight of it. It was Hera's hands who killed them, not yours...' I said, with my heart torn into pieces.

'That's exactly what my good friend Theseus said. He was the only one who was brave enough to see me after this bloodshed. You see, a great curse is inflicted upon everyone who soaks their hands in innocent blood. No one comes near them in fear of infection. But Theseus took me with him to Athens. He made me his guest, and he helped me recover. "Only heroes can endure hardships" he used to say, and I stopped considering suicide anymore.'

That's right! This is the brave and warm-hearted hero I met a while ago. After a long string of bad luck, Hercules luckily had the support of Theseus. I remembered what Zeus had told me just before vanishing: 'some things are common in both worlds'. I was now realising that friendship was one of those things.

THE LERNAEAN HYDRA
AND HER COUNTLESS HEADS

Of course I didn't say any of these things to Hercules. He was on fire, so I let him continue:

'I stayed with Theseus for some time, but I knew that I had to atone for this crime, if I wanted to live my life. This is why I went to the Oracle of Delphi. Pythia directed me to Mycenae, to my cousin Eurystheus, and she instructed me to serve him for twelve years. He would sentence me to twelve difficult labours. This way, I could purify my sin, and restore my reputation. So, here I am...' he sighed.

'Twelve labours?' I asked. I was puzzled. 'You mean killing this invincible lion, and ridding a whole land of it, is not enough already?'

He smiled a grim smile.

'I am not in a position to judge the oracle. I must obey and complete every single task assigned by Eurystheus, no matter how difficult.'

His piety was breaking my heart. He had taken full responsibility for his actions, but...the Sherlock Holmes in me was suspecting something else was going on. Something smelled bad about this oracle. Twelve whole years full of dangerous labours for something he was not even responsible for?

'Who is this Eurystheus anyway?' I asked suspiciously.

'He is a midget really, both on the outside and on the inside. He is sneaky and evil. If it wasn't for a trick of Hera's, the king would be me, not Eurystheus. It is to this goblin that the oracle has forced me to go to, and fall to his knees and beg him to accept my submission! I hope you know how humiliating this was...'

All I know is that if I was the strongest man on earth, I would punch Eurystheus into space orbit! But I said something else instead:

'All I know is that you are the righteous one, and he is dishonest.'

He gave me a warm smile:

'Tim, my friend, I am not as innocent as you might think. There is a reason why trouble is after me all the time. This was not the first time I soaked my hands in blood. It has happened before, but no god was to blame for that one...'

He realised I was baffled, and added:

'When I was a young boy, my adoptive father did all he could to give me the best education. The brightest teachers tried to shape me from a shallow creature into an intelligent man...'

'And?'

'Well. I couldn't make sense of anything except for things relating to physical strength and sports. Concentration and studying were my worst nightmares...' (I have to admit: He was right about this one!) 'A great musician, Linus, tried to teach me music. How absurd. Because of my objections, he would punish me by forcing me to "play" the lyre for hours on end. At some stage, he was fed up with me, and decided to hit me. You see, I lost my temper after this. I smashed the lyre on his head! Poor Linus dropped dead. I didn't realise how strong this blow was. My father panicked, and sent me to Mount Cithaeron. There, in the roughness of this land, with all these wild animals, the shepherds and the herds, I felt at home. It was there that I made my club and killed the lion I am wearing.'

'Maybe, Hercules, your physical strength is your greatest weakness...' I thought out loud. He was surprised by this statement.

'And you, Tim, even though you're just a little boy, you have a very strong...mind!' he said. He was proud of me. A kind heart was beating under these lethal muscles.

'What are you planning to do now, Hercules?' I broke the ice.

'I will take this lion skin to Eurystheus to prove that I have completed this labour, and then I will receive instructions for the next one,' he said like discussing his daily routine.

He loaded the massive skin on his shoulders, and set forth.

'Something tells me I will need your power too,' he said with a meaningful smile.

The setting on my screen changed all at once. The sun dipped behind the horizon and the light hid under the heavy mist. Only a hill top now stuck above the grey veil of fog. I zoomed into the picture and I "entered" the mist: it felt sickly. You could only smell danger and death in here. In the midst of this blur, I picked out a lake. Its surface was still and its waters murky and unfriendly. Swamps and marshes were spreading everywhere around. Thank goodness I didn't need to walk in this place. I was looking at the lakeshores for signs of life, but nothing was moving. Whilst looking around, I came upon a gruesome scene: a pile of mainly human bones and skulls was standing half-sunk into the muddy water. I thought that whatever it was that created this horrific collection, it would definitely be Hercules's next target. But the strong hero was nowhere to be seen. A small river caught my eye. It was like a snake made out of water, and it linked the lake with the foot of the hill. I followed its course with my finger, and I reached a spring that gushed out from the mouth of a deep cave on the base of the hill.

Suddenly, I saw flames of fire shooting up through the reeds near the spring. When I approached, I came across Hercules and a younger man.

'Welcome Tim! This is my nephew Iolaus. He wanted to come and help me slay the Hydra, the beast of Lake Lerna. This is my new la-

bour. Apparently, the Lernaean Hydra is a gigantic nine-headed water-serpent; her mouths breathe fire and her noses snort out poisonous fumes,' said Hercules with such a happy smile, you'd think he was describing a school trip! The young man greeted me kindly, and threw some more wood on the fire.

'Why did you start a fire?' I asked curiously.

'Hercules wants to heat his arrows before shooting them into the dragon,' explained Iolaus.

'I will first injure her by launching my arrows from afar, and when the monster weakens, I will cut off her heads with my sword,' planned Hercules.

'How about the poisonous fumes and the blazing fire? What will you do about these?'

'We will soak our clothes and we will cover our mouths and noses with wet cloths,' said Iolaus.

This sounded like a good plan. But before seeing the actual monster, we could only guess what it would be like. Just the fact that I happened to "be" there, was already a bad sign...

I didn't have time to finish my thoughts: a creepy symphony of loud swishing sounds was heard coming out of the cave. A horrible beast slithered through the opening, blocking it with its bulkiness. It must have been the smoke of this fire that attracted it. The Hydra's nine heads were spread out, breathing flames in every direction. Her large body was twisting and writhing, stirring up the spring's muddy waters. As soon as she caught sight of Hercules and Iolaus, she braced herself for an attack.

Hercules didn't hesitate for a minute. He had already placed his burning arrows on his bow and he was shooting them at the monster in groups of three. The Hydra was stunned at this first attack. She stepped back in pain by slightly pulling her body away, but her nine heads quickly sprang forward.

The air was suffocating. The smoke from the blazing fire blurred the already misty atmosphere, concealing both the monster and the two men. As soon as the heads rushed forward, I saw the sword of Hercules glimmer and...whoosh! It landed against one of them. The blood sprayed out of the chopped head. The snake seemed to be out of control. But soon after, two new heads grew from the neck stump!

Hercules and Iolaus were cutting off every single head that was rushing upon them. The whole snake withdrew for a couple of seconds only to come back stronger. Only then, the horrible outcome of this attack became clear: on each stump there were now two new heads. Eighteen dangerous fire-breathing mouths were now storming against the two men. The poisonous fumes coming out from their noses were already making Iolaus sick. I was anxiously watching him lose his balance, and I realised that he would soon pass out. This didn't seem to be a problem for Hercules, who was nevertheless coming to a dead end. He realised that he couldn't keep on chopping heads, because this was making things multiply from bad to worse! This was an extremely difficult situation. As soon as he realised that his nephew was losing control, he grabbed him with one hand, lifted him up and backed away. They retreated to a secure spot just behind the fire they had started, where Iolaus managed to get back to his feet again:

'Unbelievable! Instead of defeating the monster, we made it even stronger!' he said full of despair.

'This doesn't look good, guys,' Hercules said anxiously.

Let me tell you something: I was pretty upset! How come no one had warned these two brave warriors about Hydra's "minor" anatomical peculiarity? The Sherlock Holmes in me woke up again. These tasks given to Hercules by Eurystheus were not just difficult. They were impossible. They were death traps! That's it! This would be the end of it! There was definitely a solution. Definitely...

I replayed the scene of beheadings in my head. The blood that was squirting out of each of the open stumps was feeding a new, living head. All we had to do was find a way to stop this bleeding and "numb" each neck stump.

More hissing and swishing was suddenly heard. It was louder than Hydra's first appearance, and it was coming closer and closer to the two men. I had to be quicker than this. Wait. Cauterising! This is what stops bleeding! I remembered this movie where someone was injured but couldn't receive any care or medicine. He had stopped the bleeding by scorching his wound with a heated metal tool.

I turned to Hercules and Iolaus. The hero's young nephew couldn't afford the strength for another encounter with the beast.

'Hercules,' I exclaimed, 'I think I can help you finish off the Hydra...'

I told him about my plan. After making sure his nephew was safe, Hercules went back, clenching his sword. I "grabbed" a firebrand with my finger, and waited.

Hercules decided to hide until the Hydra appeared again. When one of the eighteen heads rushed upon him, he said: 'Now!', and cut off one of them. I immediately stuck the firebrand on the fresh wound. A creepy screech was heard. In the midst of this smoke, we couldn't see much. But when the snake re-emerged, we could clearly see the neck stump. Nothing had grown out of it!

The test was successful, but we would have to repeat it seventeen more times!

'Let's not rush, eh?' said Hercules. 'We must make sure that you have enough time to scorch each stump after me chopping off the head.'

'Yes. You must also make that you will dodge the rest of the heads, whilst not burning yourself, and whilst keeping an eye out for surviving poisonous fumes,' I thought, but kept it in.

Everything that followed made me bow before his strength, but also before his reflexes and his stamina. Yes. This was definitely the greatest hero of all times! Despite his bulkiness, he was leaping and twisting like a skilful dancer. He would cut off the head that was closer whilst dodging the rest. He was incredibly fast!

Iolaus was dying to help him. He collected more of the blocks of wood, and threw them on the fire. This way, as soon as Hercules exclaimed 'now!', I was already armed with a firebrand, which I could then immediately slide to the stump.

In the end, the "now!"s that were heard were nineteen...It was not Hercules's fault at all, nor Iolaus's. As it happened, at a certain point I missed a stump. As a result, we got two new heads, while I ended up scorching the mane of the lion skin, hanging over the hero's back! But, it all ended up well in the end. Or...did it?

The heads were lying all around on the ground, and the snake wasn't moving anymore. But it was with horror that we noticed one of the heads still writhing. Hercules grabbed it from the neck as if he was doing the most natural thing in the world, and then sighed with fatigue:

'Guys, I forgot to mention: one of these heads is immortal. We cannot kill it...'

Iolaus and I...we couldn't believe this...My finger was exhausted from the constant sliding and scorching! Hercules realised how tired we both were. He picked up a big stone and placed it on the head he was holding. He then said:

'Tim, my friend, can you just hold this stone over here?'

I pinned it in place with my other finger (the fresh one), whilst Hercules set about digging. He dug a massive pit - so massive I couldn't even see him anymore. He then jumped out and said:

'All right, Tim. You can release it now.'

When I lifted my finger, the hero grabbed the head again and hurled it in the hole. It couldn't really go anywhere; it was just bouncing around, at the bottom. Hercules then asked Iolaus to follow him, and together they climbed towards the top of the hill. Just when I was wondering how on earth he managed to climb after all this, I suddenly saw him rolling an immense boulder! He pointed towards the pit, and then let it go down the slope. The boulder's fall shook the whole hill and rolled down straight into the hole, sealing it for good! Now tell me: how could I explain to Hercules that, amongst everything else, he was also a... super-golf champion?

'That should be ok now, I think,' said the hero, after making sure that the large rock was stuck there for good.

He then took back his arrows, and after slicing the snake in half, he dipped them in the poisonous blood.

'These arrows are now deadly,' he explained. I thought: Was this really such a good idea? I couldn't make my mind up.

'Tim, I would like to thank you with all my heart for your help. As well as you, my nephew!' said the kind-hearted hero. He then picked up a few of the dead heads and, announced:

'Let us now sacrifice these to the gods who helped us! And then, let's go for a bite. I really feel like a barbecue after seeing all these flames!'

Drained from all this hard work, Iolaus gave me a meaningful look, and we both burst into laughter.

THE DEADLY STYMPHALIAN BIRDS

The two men disappeared into the mist and the picture on my screen moved upwards. The smoke coming from the fire and the sickly mist gave way to a deep-blue sky with white, fluffy clouds. The gate of the Olympian palaces flashed like gold under the bright sunlight. A familiar figure, the goddess of wisdom, came close. She fixed her incredible piercing deep-blue eyes upon me whilst her calm voice was heard welcoming me:

'Hello, Tim! I am glad to see you again.'

'Me too, ehm, Ms Athena,' I was a bit embarrassed because I remembered the time when, whilst Poseidon was flooding her city, I called her just by her name.

'Tim. We have shared all these experiences together. I believe we can be less formal now. You can call me Athena,' she told me softly. The goddess ignored my embarrassment, and went on:

"I reckon you have suspected already: I am one of the gods that help Hercules. The strongest mortal of all has been through a lot, as you may know, but there is still a long away ahead. More difficult tests and a painful ending...'

Athena realised I was rather upset about this, so she hastened to explain:

'Don't worry though. This is just a way for him to cut through the difficulties and take up his position in the world of gods more quickly...'

So he won't end up in the Underworld, the world of the dead...Does this mean he will become a god? I haven't heard of that before.

'Yes!' said Athena. 'Hercules will honour the name of our father. He will reach great glory and fame, and he will achieve immortality. There is a seat in our world waiting for him.'

But again, I couldn't understand why one had to suffer so much for a good reward...

'He wouldn't want it otherwise. Actually, the greatest reward is that with his achievements, he will become an example of bravery and kindness for the rest of the mortals. Heroes can't be bothered about hardships because they are interested in honour and glory. Do you remember Theseus's words? 'Only heroes can endure hardships', he once said; and Hercules, is the greatest hero of all. He has to face the toughest challenges.'

The picture of the giant man with the big muscles came to my mind, and I felt that Athena was right after all.

'How about Hera? How "honest" is her part in all this?' I asked quite angrily.

'You have your suspicions, and very rightly so. It's true that Hera asked Pythia to send Hercules to Eurystheus. She is behind the twelve impossible labours. But, don't forget that no one is above Zeus, and he has made sure that Hercules won't be alone in this struggle. This is where you come in. If you wish, you can help him for the last time, in one more labour.'

Of course I do. Where would I get another chance for something like this?

'And what would that be?' I asked. I couldn't wait for it.

'He must defeat the Stymphalian Birds.'

'Birds? Is it little birds that the hero has to kill?' I responded humorously.

'If by little birds you mean man-eating birds with beaks of bronze, nails that cut through the flesh, and sharp metallic feathers that launch at their victims, then yes!' Athena said in all seriousness.

I thought: thank you very much I won't have any of this! I don't think I can stand even the idea of such little birds! But I didn't have the time to respond after all... A shadow fell over Athena. A large black vulture was sweeping circles over her head. The goddess, completely oblivious to this scene, turned to me and said:

'Tim, let me introduce you to my brother, Ares. He is the god of war.'

The vulture swept down and landed right in front of her. It was then transformed into a tall muscular man, with black hair and a helmet on his head. He was wearing armour and he was holding a spear. He ignored me completely. His black wild eyes pierced Athena darkly.

'I couldn't care less about this mortal midget!' (How polite of him!) 'What is this about? Did I just hear that Hercules will go to Stymphalia to kill my own birds?'

'Your lovely little birds, my brother, are spreading the fear of death and disaster everywhere around Lake Stymphalia,' she pointed out to him.

'Well, this is their job!' said Ares, full of despair, as if he was wronged by everyone.

What a pleasant guy! How sweet of him!

'You know very well that we gods shouldn't just act randomly,' Athena told him calmly. 'We must keep a certain balance in the world of the mortals. That's enough now. Your stupid birds have caused enough trouble. The labour has already been assigned, and Hercules will honour the divine oracle.'

Ares went ballistic. His eyes were shooting out flames of anger. He struck the ground with his spear, causing the Olympian palaces to shake. But then, a frightening thunderbolt tore the clouds apart and

struck his spear, making him fall back. He was shocked. Zeus had spoken once again by offering rather convincing arguments!

'Don't you have a war to go to?' Athena said with scorn.

The angry god of war murmured something through his teeth and was transformed back into a vulture. He spread his wide, large wings, and disappeared into the clouds.

'Ignore this troublemaker! I win our battles all the time and he has been holding a grudge,' Athena smiled. 'Anyway...I will protect Hercules from the lethal feathers of the Birds and he will take over all the rest. And you, if you need a certain kind of "tool", you now know that there is someone who will happily help you...,' said Athena with a meaningful smile, and disappeared into a golden cloud.

Oh well. I was used to being left alone with all these questions. I just stayed there, simply gazing at the screen picture which rolled downwards again, all the way back to the ground. In the end, it "landed" on a place as haunted as Lerna. The fumes and the mist aside, this landscape was almost the same: a large hostile lake, surrounded by dangerous swamps and a hill. The place was full of bones that once belonged to poor humans or animals. However, vegetation here was very dense. At least these little bird-monsters were not snorting out burning flames of fire! On the other hand, you couldn't really tell what was hiding behind the thick forests spreading out into the dirty swamp waters!

I searched for Hercules. It didn't take long to pick out his muscular frame sitting on the hill. He was all alone, dripping with sweat. My heart was torn into pieces at the thought of Athena's words. Chances were I wouldn't see him ever again after this. The goddess had told me that this would be the last time I was helping him walk this difficult path. I decided to push away all these sad thoughts, and I greeted him warmly as if nothing was going on:

'Hello again, Hercules! What is the matter? Where is Iolaus? You didn't bring him with you for this labour?'

'Hello to you, my little friend! No. You see, I didn't want him to risk his life just like that,' he said with a sad expression.

'Just like that? What do you mean just like that?'

'I mean Eurystheus, this sneaky slug...he refused to acknowledge my last labour. He told me that slaying the Lernaean Hydra didn't count, because Iolaus helped!' he huffed and puffed.

I think that Eurystheus should hang out with the Nemean lion and the Lernaean Hydra! Of course this guy was so dodgy, he wouldn't say anything about Hera's "friendly part" in this well-planned "Twelve ways to die" game! Luckily, Hercules had both divine and...mortal help at his disposal!

I took some time to observe the hero. He was even more drained than the last time I saw him. His hair and his beard had grown so much that wild birds could well be nesting in there! This made me think of the horrible little birds of Ares, and this was probably the scene of the new labour.

'You must have been here for quite a while, no? I asked. 'Oh, and by the way, where exactly is "here"?'

'This is Lake Stymphalia, in north-east Peloponnese,' replied Hercules, 'and yes you are right: I've been here in this inhospitable place for many days. I am trying to kill the man-eating Stymphalian Birds, but I haven't made it yet. I am hoping that, now that you are here, I will be luckier.'

'What is the problem here? Can't you just shoot them with your arrows? Are you at risk of being attacked, you think?' I asked. Could it be that Athena wasn't offering enough protection?

'I think the gods are helping me, because the sharp feathers they throw at me don't reach me at all,' he dismissed my assumption. 'But, no matter how much I lurk, no matter how many I get to shoot, there are so many of them, that it just never ends! I did shoot some of them in the beginning with great success. But now that they know they are in danger, they are hiding inside the swamp's rich vegetation. I can't see them. It's impossible,' he sighed.

'Did you try frightening them into the air?'

Hercules's face brightened up:

'Great Idea! But how are we going to do that?'

I was thinking of "super-golf".

Our minds connected immediately. The hero answered his question himself:

'I will roll a few large rocks down this hill, just like I did in Lerna! The loud noise will frighten them for sure!' he exclaimed.

Without another word of delay, he started looking all around. But in this place, there were not many large rocks. The hero picked up the largest he could find, and as soon as he let it roll down the slope, he grabbed his bow and his arrows. The rock made plenty of noise, until it finally crashed into the lake. A few Stymphalian Birds swarmed over the spot where the rock had fallen, and Hercules started shooting his arrows. These birds were truly horrible with dangerous large "hooked" beaks of bronze, flashing in the air. As soon as they flew over the lake, they unleashed their blade-feathers creating a lethal mini-rain.

Thank heavens Hercules possessed a skilful aim. Each arrow struck straight at its target. But the horrid squawking was still heard from all around, meaning that the Birds hiding were still quite many. Hercules tried rolling more rocks, again and again. He killed a few more, but most of them were obviously still lurking in the swamp. That was it. He was fed up and he felt hopeless: 'Tim, I don't think I can make it this time. I can't make them come out, so I can't kill them. Even if I stay here for years, I won't be able to finish them off. If only I had something that could really frighten them... a tool or something that would make them fly into the air. This would be our last hope...' he wept.

A tool? When was the last time I heard something about a tool? Ah yes! Athena had mentioned that if I needed some special tool, she could help me find one...Oh yes! Hephaestus! This great inventor, the

super-craftsman of gods and humans, the "source" of all tools! What if...Before finishing my thoughts, a white piece of cloth covered my screen. It was not a dress though...it was rather like...a curtain. A metallic female hand (!) appeared and pulled the cloth aside. She was one of Hephaestus's robot-maids. She bowed politely, and let me in with a gesture. I was once again inside the workshop of the masterful god. But there was no smoke or fire this time. On the contrary: the place was surprisingly neat and orderly...

The robot-maid disappeared into the depths of the workshop and I ended up all by myself. Actually, not really ...The rest of the maids were standing around everywhere, but completely motionless, fixing their large cold metallic eyes on me, and "smiling" politely with their bronze lips. This whole thing was creepy...I looked at them more carefully and I noticed that they were all wearing some sort of metallic screws in their ears; something like...earplugs!

I have to say: hanging out with mythical gods and heroes can never be boring!

'Tim! Welcome!' said the giant god with his booming voice. Hephaestus emerged from the depths of his workshop, just behind the robot-maid. He fixed his joyful eyes on me, and added:

'Did you notice? I asked my maids to spruce up the workshop. It was such a mess....'

'If I may, Mr Hephaestus, what are these things in their ears?'

'Oh! I forgot about those, ha ha!' The god signalled them to remove the earplugs sticking out of their metallic ears, and they obeyed. How bizarre...Was he experimenting with something?

'No, my dear friend. We just had a mini side effect after my last invention...'

The god was in high spirits... Come on, stop torturing me, and tell me what is going on!

'Ha ha! I will explain, Tim. But first things first. Here is the help that you and Hercules asked for in order to defeat those silly birds of the bully, Ares!' he said by revealing something under a cloth. On his table, sat two metallic dishes with something like handles at the bottom - like saucepan lids.

'Did Hera order new cookware?' I teased him.

The god laughed so loudly that the maids almost lost their balance.

'Bless you, Tim! You are such a joker! These are not saucepan lids, my boy. They are special cymbals!'

Oh, I see! Everything is so much clearer now...you should have told me earlier...

Hephaestus couldn't stop laughing at my reactions. In the end he finally explained:

'If you strike these metallic discs together, they produce a high-pitched sound that will frighten the Stymphalian Birds out of their nests. I was watching poor Hercules struggling so much without any results. Athena warned me that you would ask for my help. So I spent all day today trying to achieve the best possible sound frequency...'

'How about the...earplugs?' I asked curiously.

'Oh yes! My poor maids fell out of sorts after all these sound tests. One of them started beating the other, and then they all ended up fighting one another! I had to retune them, and I sealed their ears; I also asked them to clean up the place!'

Hephaestus took the cymbals and placed them out at the edge of my screen.

'There you are, Tim! You're ready!' he said.

Two super-plates that can send out electromagnetic waves. This "tool" is amazing!

'Can I try them out?' I asked full of excitement.

'By the name of Zeus, no! Do you know how much scolding I have received since this morning from the Olympian gods? These experiments were so deafening, that most of the gods had to shut themselves inside their temples. Imagine...'

'How about us then? How are we going to survive this deafening sound?'

'Don't worry, little Tim. Human ears are unable to hear these frequencies.'

'How about Ares? Won't he be mad at you?'

'He knows that Zeus is above everything and everyone. Besides, he owes me: I was the one who made all his weapons, his armour and his chariot!'

This Hephaestus was really a super-talented guy!

'Thank you for your kind words, my little friend. Good luck with it!' he said with his loud voice, and the divine workshop disappeared from my screen.

I was now in Stymphalia again. Hercules was sitting exhausted under a tree. As soon as he saw me, he got up quickly. He was really worried.

'I was looking for you, Tim! Is everything all right?'

'I just got the tool we need from Hephaestus!' I said full of cheer. 'Brace yourself for some serious arrow shooting!'

Hercules immediately cheered up! He prepared his bow and he stood right at the edge of hill over the lake. With my two fingers, I grabbed the plates from the corner of the screen and I crashed them together as hard as I could.

I didn't hear anything myself, but the crash caused an extraordinary sound wave that expanded through the air in circles, moving over the lake and spreading around the whole area. The reeds and the trees began to bend, and the waters raised tsunami-like circles that covered the swamps! The Stymphalian Birds squawked really loudly, and flew into the air in great panic.

The frightful swarm of flying birds blocked the sunlight and the whole area suffered a heavy rain of black blades. Hercules was passionately shooting his arrows non-stop. Dozens of dead birds were falling into the lake, until its surface filled with their horrible carcasses. In the end, just a few of these Birds that had survived, flew far away scared, until they disappeared into the horizon. Silence prevailed and the sun emerged through the clouds, shining victoriously.

Hercules dropped his bow and jumped for joy!

'We made it, Tim! We made it!' he was screaming out, but sat down after a while, exhausted

and in need of some rest.

'You know, Hercules,' I said reluctantly, 'I don't think you will need my help again. You will have the gods by your side,' I hastened to say. It was time to say goodbye. The hero bowed his head.

'Honestly, you were a god-sent gift, my little friend,' he said with his eyes fixed on the ground. 'It wasn't just about precious help. I was taught two important lessons from you: never judge someone from their appearance and use the power of your mind!'

'Thank you!' I said. I was touched. 'It was such an honour to have helped the greatest hero of all.'

But then, dark thoughts about his bad ending came back again. He realised I was feeling "down" all of a sudden and he asked:

'What are you thinking? Why so sad?'

'Nothing. It's just that I can't stop thinking about all these difficult trials that await you...' I replied.

With a joyful jump, he leapt back to his feet; he stood up, fixed the lion coat on his back, and proudly announced:

'Don't worry about me, little Tim. Danger and hardships can't bring me down. All I want is to do exactly what I am doing now: use my strength for a good cause. I know that whatever happens to me, it will actually be a way to honour my name and the name of my father, Zeus. And maybe one day, I will also be honoured with meeting the Olympian family,' he said, fixing his eyes on the deep-blue sky.

'Something tells me, Hercules,' I said as casually as possible, 'that your wish will come true. Good luck!'

In good spirits, the hero waved his massive hand goodbye. With his weapons on his shoulder, he began descending the hill like a bulky animal. Just like that time when I met him at Delphi. I was watching him getting smaller and smaller, until the screen blurred. But this time, it was not the picture. It was my own eyes.

SETTING SAIL WITH ARGO
FOR A MISSION IMPOSSIBLE

I rubbed my eyes and looked around, embarrassed...Luckily, no one saw. I suddenly heard someone whistling a happy tune. I looked around again: nothing. I couldn't see anyone. I realised that the happy whistle was coming from the tablet. Against a deep-blue sky, pictured on my screen, there were now a man's toes; they were carelessly moving in time to the whistle. A butterfly entered the scene and sat on the big toe. I zoomed out: the foot was wearing a winged sandal and it was crossed over another similar "winged" foot...

'Don't be sad, mate, life is beautiful! Especially if it's coming with the bliss of immortality...'

'All right Hermes. Got it,' I said wistfully. I was in a bad mood. I couldn't take this right now!

The god jumped up at once. He rubbed his chin with scepticism, and peered into my face:

'Let me tell you something, Tim. I know exactly what you need! And I

have the perfect recipe for it!' His hands started "cooking" an imaginary meal: 'First, we find ourselves one of the most famous voyages of all times. Then, we add several helpings of adventure and dangerous challenges to make our mix bind together. We sprinkle with supernatural creatures, a dash of magic and a few riddles. And finally, we spread an exciting treasure hunt for gold over the top, and we garnish with a super-vessel that goes out on sea, and on land! And all of these, you will get to enjoy with the most famous heroes of all times!' he triumphantly exclaimed.

'I have to admit: your offer is very enticing. I didn't really know you were such a good cook!' I teased him.

Hermes celebrated my reaction by turning a somersault in the air.

'Yes! Yes! Ladies and gentlemen! Our dear Tim, the Tim we all love! He is back again!'

I couldn't help but laugh. Let's be honest here: even if I could taste half of this "recipe" he just described, that would be amazing!

'I'm all ears!' I said, impatiently.

Hermes sat down again and resumed his secretive tone of voice:

'So! My mortal friend! Here is what we have so far: the main hero of this long adventure is Jason, a very brave and admirable boy. He is the king of Iolcos, a city in Thessaly, and like Perseus he has a similar story to tell. His uncle, Pelias, usurped the throne, to the exclusion of Aeson, Jason's father.' (What is this obsession over thrones? Are they covered with honey?) 'Aeson, in order to protect his son, had decided to send young Jason to Mount Pelion, to be raised and educated by the well-known centaur Chiron...'

'Woah, woah, wait a minute Hermes! What is a centaur?' I interrupted the god.

'The Centaurs are a wild tribe that dwell in Pelion. They have the upper body of a human, and the lower body of a horse. Chiron is an exception really. He is a very wise and prudent teacher, and he is responsible for the education of many great heroes, including Jason, whom he taught how to fight with the sword, the spear and the bow, but also disciplines of music and literature. Jason stayed with him until he turned twenty years old, when he returned to Iolcos to claim the throne from evil Pelias. The rest of the story, he can tell you himself...' said Hermes, and leapt to his feet and dashed away.

Oh dear...This god is quite unbelievable. He walked out on me yet again! As if he was running out of battery!

'Come on, don't be so grouchy. You will meet Jason, as soon as I am out. I spoke to him about you and he knows how great you are. Have fun! Oh! Before I forget! Athena asked me to tell you that when things feel too "tight" - she actually stressed the word "tight" - you should be the one who intervenes, in place of her...' said Hermes ambiguously. As usual...He then performed a ridiculous move by flapping his hands like a butterfly and flew away.

I stayed there, gazing into the countryside. A buzzing noise sounded. I headed, with my finger, towards the source. The vegetation was getting thicker and thicker. Suddenly, next to some tall plane trees, I saw a narrow stream, running with frothing and churning water. At the edge of its bank, a young man was knelt down, drinking water. He stood up and at once looked at me. Of course...Another bad-looking hero with a slightly-built body!

'Jason, is that you?' I checked. (No, this is a statue that came to life and just passed by to drink some water...)

'Yes! You must be the one and only Tim! God Hermes himself told me so many nice things about you!' (That's right! Someone needs to boost my confidence too! It was going down the drain lately, with all these super-heroes...) The "statue" went on: 'However, I also know first-hand about the help you offered to two heroes, who I am honoured to call friends: great Theseus, and legendary Hercules! I am so glad to meet you!'

'Really? Do you know Theseus and Hercules?' I was pleasantly surprised.

'Of course! I was actually on my way to meet them and ask them to join me for a difficult expedition I had undertaken.'

'Yes, Hermes did mention something about you and Pelias, but he stopped halfway. What happened? Did he give up the throne?'

'No...,' Jason replied wistfully. 'He is clenching the throne like a shell sticking tightly to the rock! He said he would only give up the throne if I manage to bring back the Golden Fleece to Iolcos.'

'And what is this Golden Fleece?'

'It is my city's holy symbol: it is the skin of a gold-hair ram belonging to Hermes. It is held in a land far away, in Colchis, by the Black Sea. As of today, no one has ever dared to travel that far. But I am determined to try,' said Jason.

There we go. Treasure hunt for gold: check! A promising long voyage: check!

We were interrupted by a strangled sound, something like whining. It was coming from the banks of the stream, further down.

Jason headed towards the source of the sound, and I followed. There, we saw a tiny withered old woman:

'What is the matter, granny?' he asked sweetly.

'Oh dear boy,' she said, 'I must go to the village on the other side of the stream, but rain has caused the river to rise and I can't cross it. What will I do? My husband is ill and he is waiting for me...'

'Don't worry, granny,' said Jason, 'I will help you cross the river. I will take you on my back.'

I have to admit: this Jason was a true gentleman! But his good intention and his strong arms were not enough. I could see from above how deep and swift-moving these waters were. Chances were, they would both end up drowning.

'Jason! Wait!' I screamed, while he was already carrying the old woman on his shoulders. 'The waters here are very deep and dangerous. You might both drown!'

'Tim, I can't leave this woman just like that. I've been taught that we must help the weak and everyone who is in need. I will do my best, and may the gods give their help too,' said Jason, determined.

I can't believe this is happening right now! I have to save the hero, who has to save this granny...

'One minute,' I said, 'let me have a look further downstream. Maybe there is a safer spot to cross.'

I quickly scrolled down and followed the stream flow. Indeed! Not too far, the trunk of a tree had fallen over the river. With some luck and good balance, Jason would make it.

I pointed the spot out to him, and he headed there with the old lady in his hands. Then, he lifted her up on his shoulders again, and, step by step, he started walking along the trunk. With the extra weight of the old lady, and without being able to use his hands, it was extremely difficult to find his balance. On top of that, the trunk was wet from the rushing water, and was dangerously slippery. Centaur Chiron must have done a great job with his training. With a couple of wide strides, Jason managed to step to the other side. Phew...They were safe. What a relief...

Jason rested the old woman on the ground carefully, but before taking the chance to talk to her, - poof!-, she was cloaked by a cloud. The young man fell back. As it cleared, a familiar figure appeared through the cloud. I felt my palms getting sweaty. It was goddess Hera...

Her black, piercing eyes brushed over me, and then fixed on our speechless hero:

'Jason,' she firmly said, 'I have heard about the exquisite education you have received, but I wanted to test your good heart. I am very happy with the outcome. I would like you to know that I will also be by your side in this difficult expedition you have undertaken. I am sure you have realised that by sending you to retrieve the Golden Fleece, Pelias thinks he is sending you to your death. But, with your skills, and the help you will receive from gods and mortals...,' she looked down on me, '...you will make it through. You must first build a special ship, suitable for a long and dangerous voyage. For this, you must find the best shipwright in Greece, and with the help of Athena, you will get the boat you need. Then, you must recruit your precious companions. This must be a band of brave heroes and skilful warriors; experienced men who will be willing to join you. Your power will be their powers combined.'

Then, the goddess turned to me and pierced me with an angry look. Oh, no! Dear me!

'As far as you are concerned, Tim...' (Bye bye lovely world!) 'I will try to ignore all of these "good-natured" thoughts you are having about me, and I will only tell you one thing...' (Come on let's get this torture over with!) 'You will be asked to help Jason just a few times, during which you must prove that you deserve the trust of the gods,' she paused for a little while, and then added, 'and mine too.' What? Not in my wildest dreams could I think that I was actually earning the trust of this hard-boiled goddess!

At once, Hera was transformed into a wonderful peafowl, which opened its large wings and vanished.

Jason was super excited.

'We are so lucky! I will definitely make it this time!'

I tried to think over this new information: this special ship was obviously the super-vessel, and the precious companions were these heroes. All the puzzle pieces - or, to put it better, all of Hermes's recipe ingredients - were falling together. We were now missing only the dangers, the riddles, the supernatural creatures, and the magic. Just a few bits and pieces!

'Tim,' Jason's voice stumbled through my thoughts, 'this expedition hasn't even started, and yet, you're already helping me! Thank you so much, my friend! I should leave now. I must quickly make preparations according to Hera's instructions. Hopefully, I will see you soon.'

I said goodbye, and at once, the picture on the screen turned into a long tunnel. I noticed some kind of light at the end of it. It was coming closer and closer, really quickly. When it came close enough, I realised that it was not light, it was an eye! How bizarre!

The mystery was solved only when I zoomed out: the eye was nothing but a painting (literally!) Together with a second eye, they adorned the prow of an impressive trireme, making it look like a face. The ship was standing at the edge of a sandy beach. It was supported on large, parallel tree trunks, which formed a long ramp that ended up in the sea. The trireme seemed ready to sail, and plenty of men were already on its deck making preparations.

Wait a minute...Who is this? But, of course! Hercules! I was so happy to see him among all these men! As soon as he saw me, he waved at me with excitement.

'Hercules? Are you also taking part in this expedition?' I asked happily.

'Tim, you little crackerjack, I am so happy to see you again! I will join my young friend Jason for his expedition, and then I will head back to complete my labours. Look who's here...' he said, and used his enormous hand to point at Theseus (!), and brought him out of the crowd.

'Hello Tim, my friend!' the kind hero waved at me warmly.

I didn't even get round to returning his greeting, because Jason took over the foreground. He seemed really excited.

'Do you see this, Tim? Everything is happening just like Hera said! I found Argus, the skilful shipbuilder, who constructed this amazing vessel for us out of special pine wood from Pelion. It has fifty oars! We named it Argo, in his honour. Of course, goddess Athena gave us a hand too: Argo stands up well to salt water and to fire. Also, the crew can easily lift her up and carry her along like a feather!' said Hercules. He was showing me around with great enthusiasm, and without taking a single pause. The truth is, I couldn't take my eyes off it!

'Oh! Let me show you her most important feature: look over here, at the top of the prow...' Right at the very front, there was a branch was sticking out; something like an antenna. 'This is a piece of timber from a tree which can speak and render prophecies: the sacred oak of Zeus, from the famous oracle of Dodona. It was given to us by Athena herself. According to the goddess, it will help us navigate through, and avoid dangers!' Unbelievable! The trireme had her own GPS!

Then, Jason hastened to introduce me to his fifty - maybe more - fellow travellers.

'The Argonauts, as we like to call ourselves, are a team of bright heroes and the most skilful men of Greece,' he proudly announced. 'You already know Hercules and Theseus. Our crew also includes the sons of gods, such as Nauplius, the son of Poseidon, kings and princes, such as Peleus, but also men with unique talents, such as the popular Dioskouri twins from Sparta - Castor the wrestler and Polydeuces the boxer; also, the sons of the wind, Boreas, Calaes and Zetes - who have winged legs - and Orpheus the musician, who, with his lyre, charms even the wildest of animals. Then, we have Lynceus, whose excel-

lent sight can reach the end of the horizon and the depths of the sea,
Tiphys the helmsman...'

While Jason was taking the time to introduce me to this rare crew, I
couldn't help but feel so proud. If only my best friends were here! Or -
even better - a couple of arrogant bullies that I had in mind!

'We are ready to sail!' said the booming voice of Hercules.

The Argonauts disembarked to push Argo into the sea. Watching a
band of heroes was really impressive, but the strange thing was, they
didn't seem to be able to move the boat a single bit!

'What is going on?' said Jason. 'When Argus finished building Argo,
we transported her over here with our bare hands...Just like I told you...
like a feather....'

Even Hercules pushed as hard as he could, but the ship remained
stuck on the trunks. I couldn't understand. What kind of a super-vessel
does this? Staying put like a stubborn donkey...

It can't be, I thought. A super-vessel like this definitely has special
features.

'Jason, why don't you ask the sacred timber on the prow? It comes
from an oracle after all, no?' I asked with some suspicion.

The men looked at each other. They had nothing to lose. Jason stood in front of Argo and talked to the branch (!)

'Argo, what is it that we have to do in order to set sail?'

Some people almost burst into laughter, until the branch finally spoke with a woman's voice:

'You must simply go aboard. All of you.'

The Argonauts - including me, of course - were all speechless. Then, after recovering from the first shock, they all jumped on Argo, hoisted the sail, grabbed the oars in hand, and waited. Then, a second shock followed: the super-vessel slid down the trunks, and shot across the sea like an arrow! All of the Argonauts were now screaming with joy and excitement. Jason served everyone wine in honour of the expedition, and, from his own glass, he poured some into the sea, as a libation - a tribute - to the gods. A group of playful dolphins appeared, swimming alongside Argo, like honourable companions to her long journey. Her white sail was billowing with pride!

The quest for the Golden Fleece had just begun, and if I wasn't that prone to travel sickness, I would have loved to have been on that deck too...

SYMPLEGADES:
ESCAPING BY "A FEATHER'S" BREADTH

The screen background turned deep-blue: the Aegean Sea. Seagulls and seabirds were swirling and circling over the sea foam. It was so peaceful, at last. I went to the bar for a fizzy drink. As soon as I came back, I saw that Jason and his companions were desperately calling out for me. I had forgotten that time was rolling faster for them. What could have possibly happened?

I zoomed into the deck.

'What is the matter, brave Argonauts? Did I miss something?'

Jason was extremely excitable:

'Yes!! You missed a lot! It's been so long since we have been travelling across the land and the sea.' Jason was once again caught in an endless monologue: 'We stopped at the island of Lemnos, inhabited only by women - thank gods they were very friendly - and then, we passed by Cyzicus, where we fought very many battles. After those adventures, we ended up leaving legendary Hercules in the town of

Mysia. On the shores of Bithynia, Polydeuces boxed with a local bully, and on the shores of Thrace we came across a prophet, Phineus. The winged sons of Boreas defeated some bird-bodied monsters, Harpies, who were after him...'

'For the love of gods, Jason! You need to stop and take a breath!' Theseus laughed. He then turned to me, and said:

'It doesn't look good, Tim. Neither our bravery nor our gifts are good enough. We are coming to a dead end...'

I looked to the horizon: I could only see the blue of the sky and the sea.

'Where is this dead end? I can't see anything.'

Jason pointed to a strong, bearded young man with clear, sparkling eyes:

'Our dear friend, Lynceus, he can see as far as gods can. He has warned us of a perilous obstacle...'

A man whose eyes featured built-in binoculars: very interesting...

'Even Argo herself warned us,' said the bearded man anxiously. 'We will soon come across the Symplegades!'

If only these guys used subtitles...It would be very useful indeed...

'What is this Symplegades?' I asked.

'It's a deadly, narrow passage which we will have to cross in order to reach our destination: Colchis!' said Jason. 'It's a pair of large vertical rocks which clash together furiously, smashing everything that attempts to pass between them!'

A stone-made trap: very extraordinary indeed. If only this sea-and-land super-vessel was also...an air vessel! It could fly over these crags, just like the sons of Boreas. No harm done!

'Shh...Listen!' Theseus's voice brought me back to (their!) reality.

Everyone fell silent. From time to time, angry claps of thunder boomed out ominously; as if Zeus was hurling his thunderbolts again (you see, by now, I was quite familiar with this sound). All of a sudden it seemed, the endless blue surrounding Argo gave way to a threatening mist ...

'Guys! Oars up!' blared Tiphys the helmsman, a seafaring old salt, who was missing only...a proper raincoat and a smoking pipe!

The regular booming sound of thunder was getting louder and louder. The Argonauts remained still and silent. Only Lynceus, who could see through the mist, was counting down the distance remaining before they reached this giant trap:

'3000 feet, 2900 feet, 2800, 2700 feet...' I don't know whose feet these were, but Jason showed me the length of a foot: it must be around 30 centimetres. The countdown was painfully slow. I was biting my nails!

When the distance came down to 1500 feet, the sound of thunder clapped once again. The mist cleared away and the source of the booming sound was revealed: a huge wall, with an almost invisible slit running vertically from top to bottom. Dear me! What on earth was this? The Argonauts were remarkably calm: only their eyes gave away their fear. As far as I was concerned, I will admit: if I were actually there I would definitely have needed a baby diaper!

Tiphys immediately instructed the sailors to row in reverse. They had to keep the ship at a safe distance, to avoid drifting into the current that the two enormous rocks would cause once opening again.

Jason took a dove out of a basket. He carefully held it in his hands, and said:

'Prophet Phineus advised us to let a bird fly through the Symplegades. He said that if the bird makes it, we will too.'

I don't see how such a lightweight dove can reach the same speed as a trireme with fifty-plus people on it! However, ever since my tablet was taken over by mythical spirits, I had learned that I can't be shocked by little things like that.

An ominous rumbling was heard once the massive wall started opening again. As soon as the thin slit opened as wide as the size of a palm, Jason released the bird. It flew away, and passed through the steadily widening gap. It then disappeared completely into the depths of the Symplegades. The two rocks were now ready to snap shut again.

Just a few seconds later, we heard the booming sound of the clash. We were all anxious to see what had happened to the bird.

'There it is!' said Lynceus. The bird was very much alive, flying over the sea. Finally, it landed on the gunwale of Argo.

Jason carefully took it in his hands, and examined it. It seemed just fine; it had only lost a part of its tail feathers...

The Argonauts exchanged nervous glances. Jason announced:

'This means that we can also...almost make it!'

The crew looked hopeless.

'Jason, did you ask help from the sacred branch of Argo?' I asked.

'Sadly, it didn't give us any advice on how to pass through the Symplegades safely,' he said disappointed.

Then, I remembered the message of Athena, as given to me through Hermes: when things were becoming really tight, I had to intervene in place of her. I couldn't see how anything "tighter" than these rocks would occur.

I tried to do some logical thinking. Luckily, the snapping intervals were always the same. Hmm...

'You Lynceus, you have an excellent sight. Do you think that once you enter the Symplegades, you could tell, exactly when I ask you to, if you are closer to the entrance or the exit of the passage?' I asked.

'Easily!' said the eagle-eyed man.

'Great! Then, Jason, all you have to do is count the time it takes for these rocks to open and snap shut again. By knowing exactly how much time you have in your hands, you can then attempt passing through the Symplegades. Once you are half way through our timekeeping, and if you're closer to the entrance, you can come out again. If you happen to be closer to the exit, this means you can actually make it out!' I exclaimed.

The Argonauts were looking at me as if I was an alien. Perhaps they didn't get it? Only Jason and Theseus seemed confident about it. Jason turned towards the crew, and announced:

'Great! Let's do what Tim suggests.'

He then turned to me, and kindly asked:

'I am not sure about a tiny detail: how are we going to count the rocks' snapping?'

Ah? Oh no! Of course! How stupid of me! The invention of clocks was still a few thousand years away! Which means...Wait! Let me see my wrist. Phew...! I sighed in relief. Luckily, I was still wearing my watch. In times like these, I really appreciate technology!

'Don't worry, Argonauts,' I exclaimed. 'I have a special timekeeping tool. It's very precise. I can count the time it takes for Symplegades to open and close again.'

The Argonauts were looking at me in awe. I have to admit that I really enjoyed being admired by a band of legendary mythological heroes!

'Guys,' said Jason to the Argonauts. 'While Tim will be busy with keeping track of time, we must prepare ourselves for some hard work.' The deck of Argo turned into a buzzy hive.

I set the time to zero and remained in position, with my finger on the button and my eyes fixed on the thin vertical slit. I started timekeeping as soon as I noticed the slightest parting of the rocks. Between this, and the booming "thunder" of the clash, I had counted one minute precisely. Then, I counted the time between the clash and the next opening: two minutes. I counted again the rocks' snapping: one minute. Good. We knew exactly how much time we had on our hands. The next step was to check how fast these muscular rowers of Argo were.

'Jason, I'm ready,' I said to the head of the Argonauts. They were not familiar with this particular time interval, so we practiced, again and again, to get a good sense of what one minute feels like.

Then, I explained to Lynceus how I was planning to let him know that this was the precise moment he had to tell us if they were closer to the entrance or the exit of the passage: I would first warn him by repeating 'you're close', three times every two seconds, and then, when we would

already be half way through (that is twenty-eight seconds), I would say 'now'. To save us time, we agreed that, depending on his judgment, he would simply have to say 'forward' or 'back' for the rowers to know how they had to proceed.

After all this, Jason took a deep breath, and announced:

'Wonderful! May gods help us! Let us try then.'

As soon as the opening snapped shut, the Argonauts drove Argo towards the rocks, and stopped her at the closest and safest distance possible. The precision, with which they were steering and helming this manually driven ship, was remarkable. I started counting down until the next opening of the Symplegades. The rowers remained in position, with the oars in their hands.

'Ready..., it's opening..., now!' I shouted, and immediately the Symplegades parted again. I started keeping track of time, while Argo was already getting "sucked" into the water current created by the shift of the massive rocks. The Argonauts were now rowing, pushing Argo deeper into the passage. In just a few seconds, the ship had already moved forward with great speed. We were already half way through the available time. Lynceus had taken over the tip of the prow; with his eyes, he was "scanning" through the passage. I wouldn't want to be in his shoes: he had an exceptional gift but also the responsibility for the lives of all these heroes. When the time came, just like we had agreed, I exclaimed 'you're close' three times in a row. For a fraction of a second, all the Argonauts were exclusively counting on me and Lynceus. 'Now' I exclaimed, only to hear Lynceus shouting back 'Back'!

The Argonauts threw themselves into a frantic rowing backward, while the rocks had already started clashing together again. Would they manage to get out? I panicked! My plan was wrong: we didn't have to worry about the moment the rocks would start going back, but about the moment the passage would become so narrow, that Argo wouldn't fit in anymore! They needed some extra seconds! My calculations were wrong! How stupid of me! Look at me: I was bragging about my achievements just a while ago, and now I was putting their lives at risk! Unfortunately, there was nothing I could do now. I closed my eyes and I waited to hear the tremendous sound of a trireme crushing.

I heard nothing. I waited a bit more. I half-opened one of my eyes and I looked at the screen. Argo had come through the passage unscathed, but the Argonauts were huffing and puffing in utter exhaustion. Thank heavens; they hadn't actually realised how much they had risked their lives. But of course, they looked disappointed, having heard this "back" word...

How on earth did Argo come through this? Tiphys, the old salt, decided to address everyone:

'My dear fellows, don't be disheartened. This was just a useful test for us. When the rocks opened, I noticed that the current created in the waters is so strong, that it can actually pull us into the passage with great force. But this is not dangerous for our Argo. If we bring the prow face to face with the thin slit, we can then save precious time. Also, I noticed that while we were heading backwards, the shutting rocks pressed the water in between and created a current that pushed us towards the entrance of the Symplegades. Once we are half way through, this current has the potential to give us a similar push towards the exit. We can save even more time like this.'

I see...This is how Argo came through the narrowing passage... Thank gods! Thanks to these currents, we got some extra life-saving seconds. The Argonauts cheered up after Tiphys's speech.

'Come on, people! Let's try again!' Jason tried to encourage everyone. 'We will make it this time!'

Tiphys started instructing the rowers. The Symplegades had once again snapped shut, and Argo took a position with her prow touching on the slit of the wall. Myself, I used exactly the same method as before:

'Ready..., it's opening..., now!' I shouted, and the Symplegades parted once again. The water current rushed into the passage, pulling the ship with great force. The vessel of the Argonauts, pressed by the force of the rocks, now creaked dangerously for a few seconds. But very quickly, the slit opened enough to let Argo into the passage. I was once again half way through the countdown: 'You're close'... 'You're close'... 'You're close'... I heard myself saying; and then an anxious 'Now'! The fractions of the second between this 'now' and Lynceus's well-anticipated word seemed like hours. He finally said: 'Forward'! The oars of Argo were running up and down wildly. The Argonauts were giving all they could. The Symplegades started clashing back again. Massive amounts of water were being pressed between the rocks, forcing Argo onto an aquatic slide out of the passage. But would she make it through the rocks before being smashed by them? My heart was pounding out of my chest, as I was watching the two walls coming together! I could now see Argo appearing right at the end of the passage. I couldn't take this anymore. I closed my eyes again. Time was up. I heard a spine tingling 'krrk', followed at once by the booming shut of the clashing Symplegades! My heart stopped. So that was it, then. The Argonauts, all these gifted heroes and friends, Theseus, Jason...they all belonged to history - again. I didn't have the courage to stare at this horrific scene. So I was only left with hearing it: loud shouts and exclamations from fifty young men! I opened my eyes and I saw the crew of Argo celebrating like a group of football fans whose team had just scored a goal in the finals! Everyone was waving at me! They were moving their hands in the air and they were throwing all sorts of objects up in the air. Jason and Theseus were jumping and hopping all around, dancing like monkeys!

'What happened? I thought I heard a "krrk"!' I said, surprised.

Tiphys pointed to the edge of the

stern. A small piece of wood from the ship's "tail" had been smashed by the rocks.

'Nothing to worry about, Tim! Argus will fix it in the time it takes for you to say "Now"!' said the old salt, with his smiley moustache.

Jason signalled everyone to quieten down:

'Dear friends, we made it thanks to the gods and to Tim! Let me hear a loud cry in honour of this young clever boy!'

A rhythmical cry was then heard, something like: 'Tim' - 'Tim'. I bowed my head in respect and paused for a while, just to enjoy the moment - like a friend amongst friends. Being humble, it made it much more special.

'Next stop: Colchis!' exclaimed Jason. 'Golden Fleece, here we come!'

I relaxed back in my chair. I was pleasantly tired, as if I was rowing too...Oh no! No! I was feeling sick...Unfortunately, I would never make it to being an old salt myself!

JASON AND THE INVISIBLE ALLY

I was relieved to watch Argo taking off. Actually, I wouldn't mind it if I didn't have to watch the sea for a little while! So I was quite happy when the water was replaced by…fire! A torch, in particular! Hmm… Where was I again? Was this a cave? A maze? A cage? What kind of monster did I have to deal with now?

'Ha, ha, ha! You young little boy! Your imagination is "galloping" like Pegasus, the winged horse!' said a familiar silvery female voice. Aphrodite!

But, where was she? I couldn't see her!

I zoomed out and saw the resplendent hall of an imposing palace. It was supported by a range of columns, each adorned with a large burning torch. The whole place was covered with white marble and elaborate golden ornamentations. In the middle of the picture, I saw an old man, sitting on a grand throne. He was obviously a king. He was looking worried. He was surrounded by a noble court of men and women, who were dressed in lavish clothing. They were engaged in a very heated conversation. Aphrodite was nowhere to be seen.

A couple of guards escorted a small group of men to the centre of the hall. It was Jason with a few of the Argonauts! He was holding an olive branch which he kindly passed to the king with a respectful bow. As the hero began talking to the king, I heard Aphrodite again. Her voice covered the dialogue between the two men:

'You have disappointed me, little Timmy...' purred the goddess of beauty and love. 'Not only don't you think highly of my winged son and his arrows, but you also seem to judge me for intervening in mortal affairs...'

I was dying to find out what was happening with Jason and his companions. Had they reached their destination? Had they found the Golden Fleece? Aphrodite's intervention really didn't come at a good time... But how could I interrupt all these people in the court? Maybe showing up now wasn't such a good idea...'

'No need to worry about that. I have arranged everything: no one can see you or hear you. Just like no one can see or hear me,' said the goddess casually. 'Besides, I can tell you exactly what they're talking about. Although you haven't given me an answer yet...'

There we go again! What was I supposed to tell her? That people should be free to choose who to love?

Her face then suddenly emerged behind one of these columns that happened to be "in front" of me. She was furious. But she was really... really...beautiful, even when she was frowning! Once again, I had turned speechless, which was probably a good thing in this case. But it was already late: she had read my thoughts.

'I see! So this is what sweet little Timmy wants...People falling in love randomly...So you don't approve my interventions. All right then, young boy. Now you will get the chance to do whatever you like. As you can see, your friend Jason and his companions have finally arrived in Colchis, and they are now talking with its king, Aeetes. They are asking him to return the Golden Fleece. As you can probably guess from his grumpy face, he is not very happy about this visit. But I can also tell you something less obvious: Aeetes is all in a panic, because he thinks that these strangers haven't just come for their sacred symbol. He believes that they are there to claim his throne too!'

For heaven's sake, what is wrong with these kings and their thrones? It seems as though this is the greatest love affair of all...

Aphrodite went on:

'You're absolutely right. You can't even imagine what people are capable of doing for the sake of power. This one in particular, Aeetes, he is already drafting a plan in his mind for wiping out Jason and the Argonauts. He is of course keeping up appearances, as you can see. They are his guests after all, and they came in peace. They even offered an olive branch. But this is what he is planning on doing: he will force the young hero to choose death.'

The king was now explaining something very politely. Jason stared at him and didn't even answer back. With a heavy heart, he agreed with Aeetes.

'Did you see this?' said Aphrodite. 'He was coaxed into undertaking two impossible labours, in order to "prove" that he is a good enough hero to carry the sacred symbol. He was assigned with yoking two wild, fire-breathing, bronze-hooved bulls, all by himself, and to use them to plough the field of Ares. Then, he must sow the field with the teeth of a dragon which will be given to him by Aeetes. The teeth will immediately sprout into an army of wild, armoured warriors, which then he will have to overwhelm. Then, Aeetes "promised" that he will give him the Golden Fleece, which is something that he will, of course, not do...'

Just by looking at them, and their reactions, I realised that Aphrodite was actually doing a live description. What was the matter with these heroes, anyway? Their kindness was their ticket to the Underworld...

'For them it is rather a ticket to fame, honour and glory, little young boy. Anyway...' she said, and with a careless move, she pushed a golden lock away from her face...I was hypnotised once again! I could have stayed there and watched her forever. You could even forget your own name by doing that.

'Tim! Little Tim!' said the goddess loudly, to jolt me out of my "sleep". She then went on: '...All I'm saying is that this is a case I would normally intervene into. Here. Look. Right next to Aeetes: do you see this charming girl with the black hair and the dark look in her eyes? This is Medea, the king's daughter. She is the formidable witch and priestess of Hecate, who is a goddess of the Underworld. And this is what I would do: I would have Eros strike her with passion for Jason. With her magical powers she would then aid him in his tasks. But I decided I'm not doing anything after all! I will let you handle the situation all by yourself!' said the goddess and gave me a sarcastic smile.

That was very helpful Ms Aphrodite! Thank you very much! How on earth would I help? I was neither a sorcerer nor a god...

Aphrodite looked at me, rather sceptical.

'All right, Tim. Don't despair,' she said more softly.

'I will let you give a hand or, to put it better, a finger! You will remain invisible from everyone during the labour with the bulls, but you will be able to magically intervene with your two fingers. You have to think carefully about how you can intervene, without raising suspicions. Once Jason succeeds in ploughing the field, he will then be able to hear you and see you. And so will the rest of the Argonauts. Then, you must help them by using your mind, only...'

Oh I see! I was kind of stressed before, but now everything seems super easy! Great!

Beautiful Aphrodite was transformed into a white swan and flew away from the palace, whilst her fading, silvery voice was saying: 'I believe in you, sweet little Timmy!'

Oh dear! She wasn't just the goddess of beauty; she was the goddess of flattery too!

The scene changed once again on my screen:

Jason was in the middle of a fenced field. An iron plough was standing in a corner. A platform had been installed just outside of the fence. Aeetes and his men were already in their seats, and so were the rest of the Argonauts too. I could see from their faces how anxious they were. Next to the platform, there was a small stone-made building with a wide door overlooking the field. One of the king's servants climbed on its roof and opened the door by pulling a long latch. At once, two black charging bulls rushed into the field, snorting out flames of fire and pawing the ground with their bronze hooves. In order to avoid provoking the animal, Jason decided to stay still and hide his fear. But I could see how desperate he was. Despite his bravery and his strength, he would hardly manage two fire-breathing bulls. I had to help him as soon as possible.

One of the bulls fixed his eyes on Jason and then charged towards him.

I placed my finger between them, in order to somehow distract the aggressive animal. But the bull started charging towards...the finger! That's right! This new information was of crucial importance. I started swiping my finger throughout the field, trying to avoid the spot around Jason. The animal was following the finger frantically!

In the meantime, the second bull was also ready to charge towards Jason. The game was now getting more complicated! I placed my other finger in front of the second bull, and I started "drawing" imaginary routes. I had to control the direction of the two animals whilst also holding, at the same time, my two fingers very close to each of them, so that they don't move out of their target zones. I was trying to wear them out as quickly as I could, by taking them through the most complicated routes possible. I think Jason realised that something was going on: as soon as the bulls threw themselves into this out-of-control running, he withdrew into a corner and just waited, doing nothing. Aeetes and his court were booing him off, and the king was obviously very annoyed. What was it that made these bulls run left and right?

In the meantime, my fingers were aching. They had been overheated by the friction! I wouldn't last long. Luckily, the bulls were already showing signs of exhaustion. Their nostrils were no longer snorting fire; just some puffs of smoke here and there.

Not long after, the two bulls found themselves facing each other. That was when I thought of a new trick: I brought my fingers together. The two animals, having both focused on my fingers, were unable to see behind their target. When my fingers came together, the two bulls crashed into one another with great force. The head on impact caused them to collapse to the ground, wounded and utterly confused.

Jason grasped the opportunity at once: with a rope in hand, he quickly headed over to the bulls, and tied their legs in such a way so as to stop them from being able to run. The bulls were so tired, they didn't react at all. They hardly managed to get up and stand on their legs. With his strong arms, Jason guided them through the field, and they started ploughing at a slow and heavy pace. The field was soon filled with smooth grooves. Loud cheers emanated from the Argonauts, who were encouraging their brave friend. He was tired but he had made it! Aeetes was extremely annoyed. On the one hand he could see that something was amiss, but on the other hand he couldn't openly accuse Jason. He frowned and ordered his men to take the bulls away and pass Jason the teeth of the dragon. This was a fresh opportunity for the king to kill him. The leader of the Argonauts "sowed" the teeth into the grooves, and took a seat in a corner for some rest. Just a few seconds later, the earth started giving birth to metallic tips! They were the tips of swords. More things were coming out of the ground: iron helmets, and then the heads of warriors, their armour, their shields, their legs and their greaves. Like zombies rising out of the ground...How creepy! Within a minute, the whole field was filled with an army of bloodthirsty warriors! They were shouting battle cries and they were swinging their swords in every direction. It seemed that they wanted to make war just for the sake of war. This field belonged to Ares after all.

Jason needed help immediately. He was already drained from the plough. How could he possibly encounter a whole army?

I thought of what Aphrodite had told me a while ago: I would have to use my mind. This means that there was a sensible solution.

Oh no! The warriors were already striking their swords on their

shields. They were desperately looking for a victim to start a fight...

Think, Tim, think! All they want, these savages, is to fight someone. Anyone. Not necessarily Jason. Which means that fighting each other might be just enough for them! I had to find a way to turn them against each other. A saying came to my mind: 'Divide and conquer...'

'Jason!' I shouted. 'It's me, Tim! You can't see me. Aphrodite had to make me invisible because we shouldn't raise any suspicions to Aeetes. Listen, I have an idea: pick up a stone and throw it on one of the warriors, but only when he is not looking...'

Jason didn't say a word. He just nodded. He found a large stone, and he threw it somewhere amongst the army. The stone landed on the shoulder of a warrior who happened to be looking in the other direction. This made him fiercely angry. He turned around, screaming, and he gave a heavy kick to the warrior behind him, thinking that he was the one who struck him. The second warrior jumped up clumsily, causing his shield to knock on a third warrior, right next to him. The third one returned the knock in anger...

Within just two minutes, the warriors had engaged in an outrageous battle. They were fighting each other furiously. Each of them wanted to kill all the rest, and become the one and only victor. Everyone was fighting as ferociously

as they could. After some time, the field was filled with corpses, and the ground was filled with blood. Hmm... I thought that at the end of the day, violence is...a self-destructive force! Jason easily finished off the few warriors lying wounded on the ground. His fellows began cheering passionately. They rushed into the field, and lifted Jason up in the air. Somewhere amongst these cheers, I heard the hero saying:

'Thank you, Tim! Great idea!'

Aeetes was furious. He jumped up from his seat, and shouted out:

'Not valid! Not valid! This labour is not valid! You cheated! You were supposed to kill the warriors by yourself!'

A very relaxed Jason replied:

'King Aeetes, you never mentioned that I must kill them myself. You simply asked me to find a way to overwhelm them, and so I did. You must now keep your promise, and give me the Golden Fleece!'

'Never!' shouted the old man frantically, and ordered his guards to arrest the Argonauts. Then something strange happened: a thick mist covered the whole place, and a thick cloud cloaked the figures of the Argonauts. I couldn't see a thing. I just heard a peafowl squawking with a piercing voice. Hera was obviously giving a helping hand here. And, this time, for a good purpose.

FOR A GOLDEN PELT

As soon as the mist cleared away, I saw the Argonauts once again. But this time, the landscape around them was different. They were in a quiet grove. Vegetation was very rich here. They were surrounded by tall trees that stopped the light from coming in, and created funny playful shadows on the ground.

'Jason, can you hear me?' I tried to distract the hero.

He, and the rest of his companions, turned to see me. At once, they started waving at me with excitement. And then, they started...whispering! It was very funny: it felt like someone had lowered the tablet volume.

'What happened? Are you ok? Why are you whispering?' I bombarded them with questions.

'Tim, our dear friend!' said Jason in high spirits. 'Thanks to Hera we're still alive! This nasty Aeetes wanted to arrest us. Who knows what our fate would be, if we ended up in his hands!' (I had a very strong opinion about this, but I didn't want to interrupt him.) 'The goddess veiled us in a magical mist, and brought us over here, to the sacred grove of Ares. This is where the Golden Fleece is, so we are on our way to get it. But we know that Aeetes's men might be lurking somewhere, so we must stay extremely cautious and silent! By the way, I wanted to thank you for your precious help back in the field of Ares. I am certain that you gave me a hand with those bulls, didn't you?'

'Yes, but I had help myself: from goddess Aphrodite. Have you seen her by any chance?'

They all shrugged their shoulders. I was about to say something, but I stopped. Anyhow, I couldn't describe her perfect beauty without being considered desperate.

'What now?' I asked.

Jason sighed:

'Look, right there, at the back; do you see this glint? This is where we are going. This is where the Golden Fleece is. It's hanging from the branch of a tree, but there is a tiny problem with it... (Mind you I was trained pretty well: I could feel the "but" coming, before actually hearing it! How impressive!)

'It's being guarded by a massive, sleepless snake.'

'Sure. But both you and your companions are strong and fearless. Can't you just kill it?' (I knew the answer to that question already. I just asked to honour the custom).

'No. This snake is sacred, and so is this place. We must retrieve the Golden Fleece without using violence.' (I was almost developing prophetic skills. For example I knew that if things were bad, they would most likely get worse!)

The Argonauts followed the glint and soon ended up close to a tree, whose branches were spread wide. Glittering in the sun, the Golden Fleece, the skin of a ram covered with a fleece of curly, golden hair, was hanging from the lowest branch. Even I, was be able to reach it. The reason for the lack of any sophisticated security measures, soon became clear...In the beginning, it looked like it was part of the big trunk. But when it twisted its head and turned its eyes to us, we realised that almost half of this trunk "belonged" to this lovely little snake! Judging by its long and horrid forked tongue that tasted the air by swishing it in and out of its mouth...this snake's intentions didn't look very friendly! The only advantage was that nothing would make it leave this tree. So the Argonauts, staying clear of its territory, took the opportunity to sit down and think it over.

And so did I: so here we had a monster which, a) we couldn't harm, and b) it wouldn't move out of its territory. If we didn't have to deal with the first restriction, things would be very simple. It would only take a couple of punches, and then...bye bye snake, hello new bag! If we didn't have to deal with the second restriction, we could easily throw something at it or distract it with something; it would then leave the tree. But, taking into consideration both of these restrictions, what were we left with? Maybe singing a lullaby to make it go to sleep? Ha, ha!

Wait a minute...This wasn't a bad idea! I remembered these flute-playing, snake-charming fakirs of India. I had also heard of another case, of someone whose music would also charm the wildest of animals. Where did I hear about that?

I curiously asked Jason about it. At once, he jumped up as if stung by a bee.

'That's it!' he exclaimed. 'The solution is here, amongst us! Our magician-musician, taught by Apollo himself!' Amongst the Argonauts, he picked out a young man.

'Orpheus, my friend. You with the god-sent gift...please tell me that you have brought your lyre with you...' he begged him.

The young man immediately opened the sack he had on his back, and took out a lyre.

'I can do without water or food. But I cannot do without my lyre!' he said with a big smile.

The musician sat back near the tree, and started plucking the strings of the instrument. Everything changed at once. I felt it too: as if I was back in my mother's womb. I was in tranquil, pure bliss. All the sounds of the grove quietened down; the birds stopped chirping and all the animals paused to eavesdrop. It felt as if nature was holding her breath to enjoy Orpheus's music without missing a single note.

The snake stopped squeezing the trunk, and relaxed its head to the side. It was charmed. Jason then grabbed the opportunity and with very soft movements he approached the fleece very slowly, and removed it from the branch. The snake remained completely motionless. Orpheus went on playing, whilst the Argonauts were slowly and quietly leaving, as if performing a slow-motion dance to the music notes. The musician stayed back and finally started retreating too, but without stopping the playing of his music. They all managed to walk out of reach.

They were already out of the grove of Ares, when Hera's mist covered them once again. This was a good sign. I realised that the quest of the Argonauts was now successfully completed. After retrieving the "gold" treasure, and after going through all these adventures, the band of heroes was now left with navigating back to Greece.

I was right! Once the misty veil of Hera cleared away, I saw Argo flying over the Aegean Sea (I didn't guess it was the Aegean: Jason told me as soon as he saw me). Without pausing for a single second (as usual), he said:

'Tim, my friend. We did well in Colchis! But

ever since, it has taken us a lot of time and plenty of tasks to come back to the familiar waters of the Aegean Sea. And the perilous adventures haven't even finished yet. Right now, we happen to be at a terrible dead end. We must urgently stop at Crete, the island that is closest, for supplies. We have run out of food and water, without which we can't go on. But the problem is, that the stop in Crete is prohibited. We can't even get close because of Talos. I am not sure you know him?' (I didn't even have to interrupt: Jason's monologue was endless) 'He is a bronze giant, forged by Hephaestus and given by him to king Minos, to protect Crete from any would-be intruders. Only one vein keeps him alive: it goes from his neck to his ankle. It's not a blood vein. Some sort of bronze liquid is running in it. Talos is so huge and swift, that he can actually circle Crete's shores three times a day! As soon as he sees an approaching ship, he uproots large rocks and hurls them at it, until it is destroyed. And if any boat gets around to coming close to the shore, Talos heats himself (!), and burns it, by clasping it in his embrace. No arrow, no spear, none of the mortal powers can harm him...'

So basically, this is a super-robot! Way ahead of its time. Hephaestus never ceased to amaze us. His inventions were amazing. But how would it be possible to overcome this giant automation that he had created?

I looked at the Argonauts. Poor souls. They had probably gone through a lot, since the last time I saw them (in their own space time of course). They all looked like castaways: bony and pale, with long hair and beards. These people had nothing in common with the proud heroes that once departed from Iolcos.

I now realised that my presence

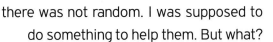

there was not random. I was supposed to do something to help them. But what?

The voice of Lynceus stumbled through my thoughts and brought me back to reality:

'Guys! There! On the shore! I can see Talos!'

The Argonauts were so lucky. The giant robot couldn't see as far as Lynceus. The ridges of Crete's mountains were slowly rising in the horizon; Argo was still far from the shore. This super-robot couldn't do anything to me, so I decided to "run" to the island before them. Shortly after, I was face to face with this massive, fearful invention. It looked human, but it had a bronze body, lifelessly glowing in the sun. His movements were automated, and with each step, he was causing a mini earthquake. He reminded me of the maids of the god-forger a little. I remembered the last time we met, and those "tests" he was doing with the cymbals, which ended up detuning his robot helpers...

Hmm... Maybe this was the solution then: since I could approach the island myself, I could use (if I could get them) the cymbals of Hephaestus to turn off or - at least - detune Talos. But even if the god was reading my thoughts right now, I don't think he would be willing to let me destroy one of his best inventions...

A thunderbolt cracked through my screen. No, it wasn't a thunderbolt after all. It was something like a snow-white colour that was flying in the air. I curiously tried to approach the spot. A bright white flying swan was glowing in the sun.

'I knew I could count on you, sweet little Timmy,' said Aphrodite. 'You did very well in Colchis! But I have to tell you something that might upset you, although it is true: if I had let Medea be shot by one of those arrows, she would now be practising her magical skills in order to easily smash Talos...'

The goddess of beauty reminded me of my mum a little: this 'I told you' phrase was her second surname! One minute though, this information is very important: does this mean that Hephaestus wouldn't go against destroying Talos?

'First of all, we, mums are always right,' purred the goddess. 'As far as Talos is concerned, he has served his purpose. The empire of Minos is now very strong and doesn't need a guard like him.'

But, then...

Maybe, I could ask a tiny little favour from honourable Hephaestus: could he please give me back these amazing electromagnetic cymbals to try them again?

The silvery, irresistible laughter of Aphrodite echoed:

'My dear husband is already aware of your wish. Actually, when he heard your thoughts about using the cymbals on Talos, he laughed so loudly, that the hammer fell off his hands! This is exactly what he said: "Oh dear! This boy's mind is as sharp a steel trap!" He definitely likes you a lot...So, my little boy, you now have a present from both of us!' said the goddess in the shape of a swan, and flew away, after dropping those amazing cymbals! Before vanishing into the clouds, I heard her say:

'And remember: we all have our "Achilles' heels"...'

I was super excited. I said 'thank you' (as loud as possible; I was in a cafe after all!). I couldn't wait. With my finger, I "ran" on the screen until it was filled by the figure of Talos. The giant robot was walking non-stop, so I had to do something very quickly, before he went too far. I grabbed the super-cymbals at once from the edge of the screen, and I crashed them together as hard as I could. This was the second time I was doing this in this cyberspace. Once again, the sound waves spread in circles afar. Talos paused his automated walking, and remained stunned. He sealed his ears with his hands, but it was already too late. His balance had been disturbed. He tried to bring forward his right leg, but in vain. It was caught bent. The metallic giant staggered, and, finally, with an unbelievable thud, he fell on the ground.

I quickly "ran" back to Argo. I explained everything to Jason, and

then the Argonauts did all they could to reach the shore quickly. I turned back to where Talos had collapsed. Luckily, it was a quiet and uninhabited coastal area. The giant robot was now completely out of tune. He was still lying on the ground and could hardly move.

On his right ankle, I noticed something looking like a screw or a plug. That was the only spot where he had something like this, the rest of his body was clear. Hmm...This could be an important switch. So we could actually switch him off completely. This would be much better of course. But pulling out this screw was dangerous. I remembered Aphrodite's last words: "We all have our 'Achilles' heel'..."

Argo was coming close. The heroes jumped out of the ship, and approached the robot carefully. Jason was amazed:

'But, Tim! How? How did you do this?' he mumbled.

'Let's say that Hephaestus is on your side,' I hastened to say, and added: 'Jason, I believe that this screw, on Talos's right ankle, is necessary for his operation. Do you think you could pull it out?'

'I am not sure, but it's definitely worth a try. If we finish him off, many lives will be saved from now on,' said Jason, whilst I once again realised what it truly meant to be a hero. The leader of the Argonauts approached the foot of the metallic giant, very carefully. As Talos was lying still, his leg suddenly twitched with great force, and moved towards Jason. The hero reacted immediately by jerking aside with a swift jump. The leg of the robot twitched again, and then remained still. Jason then stood up, and went close to Talos's ankle. He grasped the metallic screw with both hands and tried to pull it out. He tried again and again, until...The robot tried to lift his leg. The right sole left the ground and started rising. Jason was holding himself from the metallic plug. The leg was taking him with it! We all held our breath. The leg was already two meters away from the ground, when the plug loosened, together with Jason. The hero dropped on the ground and plummeted a few meters down. We were all watching anxiously: Jason was looking confused from the drop. He tried to get back on his feet again. He was alive! But the moment the plug squeezed out of the robot's

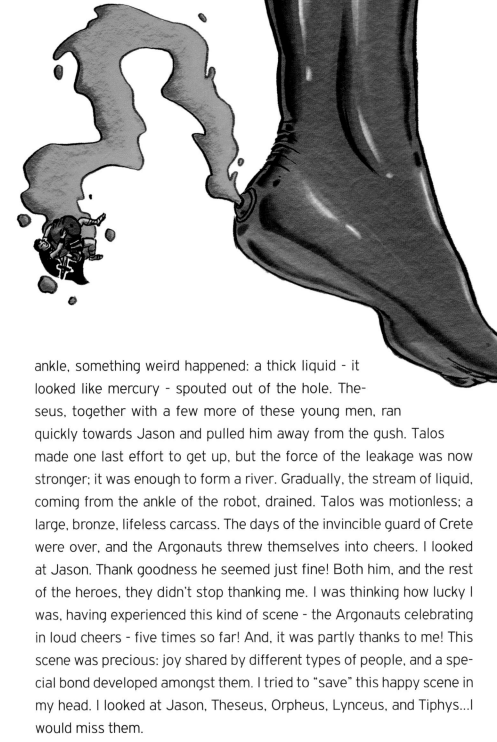

ankle, something weird happened: a thick liquid - it
looked like mercury - spouted out of the hole. Theseus, together with a few more of these young men, ran
quickly towards Jason and pulled him away from the gush. Talos
made one last effort to get up, but the force of the leakage was now
stronger; it was enough to form a river. Gradually, the stream of liquid,
coming from the ankle of the robot, drained. Talos was motionless; a
large, bronze, lifeless carcass. The days of the invincible guard of Crete
were over, and the Argonauts threw themselves into cheers. I looked
at Jason. Thank goodness he seemed just fine! Both him, and the rest
of the heroes, they didn't stop thanking me. I was thinking how lucky I
was, having experienced this kind of scene - the Argonauts celebrating
in loud cheers - five times so far! And, it was partly thanks to me! This
scene was precious: joy shared by different types of people, and a special bond developed amongst them. I tried to "save" this happy scene in
my head. I looked at Jason, Theseus, Orpheus, Lynceus, and Tiphys...I
would miss them.

Oh, for goodness sake! What was wrong with me? I resumed an upright and confident position on my seat, and I said goodbye. I was trying
to look happy and unflustered. 'I hope I will see you again,' I said. But,
something in me didn't feel right...

BACK TO NOW

'Oh! What a wonderful fifty-oared trireme!' my dad's voice made me jump up as if I was electrocuted.

'What is the matter, Tim?' my dad was standing over me with a big smile. 'You were watching this documentary, eh?'

'Ehm, yes! Yes! I am watching a documentary about the Argonauts and the quest for the Golden Fleece!' I mumbled.

'Mm! The quest for the Golden Fleece! A perilous expedition full of adventures!' (Tell me about it...)

I turned the tablet over, and, pretending to be calm, I asked him:

'How about you? Did you finish?'

'Yes! I just came to let you know that me and your mother, we are going to the museum shop for a while. Do you want to come?'

'No it's ok! I will wait here...' I quickly said.

Once my father left, I immediately turned the tablet over again. The screen pictured beautiful clouds in the golden colours of a wonderful red sunset. They soon cleared and gave way to the imposing Olympian palaces. A magnificent semi-circular, open-air space with tall shining columns opened up in front of me. I had never seen such a crowded gathering of gods! Zeus was sitting on his golden throne right in the centre, and he was surrounded by many gods; some I had met, and some I didn't know of at all. Their eyes were fixed on me. Being the centre of all these gods' attention was rather embarrassing. Luckily, I could also see some familiar faces: apart from the king of the gods, I also spotted Athena, with her calm smile and her incredible piercing blue eyes, reserved Hera, imposing Poseidon, dark Ares, mischievous Hermes (who of course winked at me in his usual secretive way), bright Apollo, smiley Aphrodite, with her staggering beauty, Hephaestus, her amazing craftsman, kind-hearted Demeter, and - yes - also there was: Hercules! Once he saw me, he started waving his massive hand to me! I hate to admit it, but I was rather moved by this gathering. I had bonded with them without even realising. They felt like they were my "people" now. It seems that Zeus was right in the end. These gods were resembling humans: they had their own whims, preferences and weaknesses; each of them a different character. And all of us together, we had shared unforgettable moments.

'Gods,' Zeus's booming voice jolted me out of this whirl. A deafening silence reigned over the Olympian palaces. 'Let us raise our nectar glasses and drink to this little mortal friend of ours, Tim!'

"Friend of ours"? Wow! I thought I was hearing the ring of a bell. Everyone raised their glasses, and their voices echoed into the clouds. The "bell" kept on ringing or...maybe this was my heart beating?

Zeus fixed his piercing eyes on me:

'So, Tim. I hope you didn't find us boring after all?' he said. I couldn't speak; I was "choking up". This was the first time, ever since I had met these guys, that I was feeling relieved that they were reading my thoughts!

I couldn't see clearly. Was it the great glow coming from the gods? Was it the sunset light reflected in the golden palaces? I had no idea. I just heard:

'Little, Tim. We are really happy about the time we have spent to-gether...(I can tell when a "but" is following, remember?) '...but it's time to say goodbye,' said Zeus, confirming my intuition.

But, just before disappearing completely, the voice of Zeus rang in my ears once again: '...or, maybe not?'

Do you want to know what happened next? The usual: my screen turned black, leaving me once again puzzled. However, this time, the black was soon replaced by the game I was playing just before com-ing to this museum. The famous "level" I had reached was right there, waiting for me to start again from where I had stopped. This seemed to me very boring now. I turned the tablet off. I didn't want to even see it anymore. I took a deep breath and let myself relax by staring at the garden. My eyes stopped at the trunk of one of these age long "Athenian" olive trees: its knobs and its marks reminded me of a code of some sort...

Wow! I was losing it! 'Come back, Tim!' I said to myself.

I got up to leave, and I bumped into my parents:

'Oh Tim, I know, you must have been terribly bored,' said my mum with an apologetic tone.

'No, it's ok...I browsed, on my tablet, through all these interesting facts about Greek mythology,' I said (it was not a lie after all!)

'I am glad you found something that sparked your interest!' said my dad (wrong: this "something" had found me, and also, the interest wasn't just sparked, it was fired!)

'Can we go now?' I asked, tired.

'Yes of course, let's go...' they both said.

We walked the stairs up to the museum's main entrance, but my mum suddenly halted:

'Listen, Tim. I know you are not really interested in museums and ancient displays, and I know that you are looking forward to leaving this place, but I wanted a little favour from you...'

Normally, this type of introduction would cause me an allergic re-action. But after this roller-coaster of mythological adventures, I was

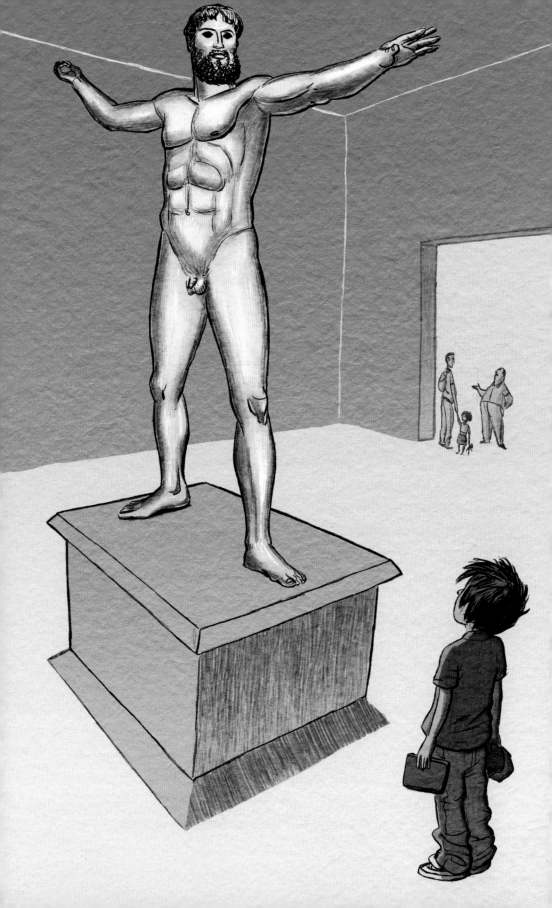

feeling like an empty bag of chips. I was too weak to react to anything. My mother went on:

'I would like to show you one thing only, just one exhibit. It is worth your time; you must see it before leaving the National Archaeological Museum. I promise, it will only take a minute...'

I think she realised how unable I was to react, because she grabbed me from my arm and, at the drop of a hat, she pulled me through the museum galleries like a shopping trolley.

'Here we are!' she finally exclaimed when we reached a large, two-meter high, bronze statue.

I first glanced at it from the back: it was a nude; a barefoot, muscular, well-proportioned man in an upright position. First thing I felt was making fun of the fact that he was naked, but the statue was too impressive for that. So I just stood there, looking at it. His hair was flowing down behind his head in braids. His right hand was raised in a throwing position, as if he was holding something, and his left hand was stretched at the front, as if he was pointing or trying to maintain his balance. Every single muscle, every detail of his body, had been sculpted so realistically, you would think the statue was ready to come to life. The man was leaning on his left leg, while his right heel was slightly raised off the ground; as if he was preparing a striking motion. What was more incredible was the ability of this heavy bronze object to stand on the pedestal connected only at a couple of points.

My mother, in the meantime, was pouring out lots of information.

'This statue is either Zeus who is about to hurl a thunderbolt, or Poseidon with his trident,' she said while pulling me over to see the statue's front side.

I stood there, right in front of this nude man, and turned into a statue myself!

'Zeus!' I mumbled.

'Yes! The majority of archaeologists agree that it's Zeus,' added my mother casually.

'It's Zeus!' I mumbled again. I was once again meeting the bearded guy who had once taken over my tablet. The father of all gods and humans, the boss of Mount Olympus, the prudent judge with his tremendous thunderbolts!

I realised that my mother was slightly worried with this reaction, so I tried to pull myself together.

'Ehm, I have seen this statue in a documentary,' I said.

'Isn't it wonderful?' she asked me, turning her eyes back on the statue.

Yes. This encounter could be called, at least, wonderful...

'Yes! This is why I wanted you to see it! Come on now, Tim. You look exhausted. Let's go...' said my mum and pulled me away. I followed her passively, while my eyes remained fixed on Zeus.

I know, I know. After spending so many hours taking part in all these "live" adventures, my mental state was not at its best. But I swear that, on my way out of the museum, I noticed a smile behind his thick beard...

THE END

THE BOOK "GODS, HEROES
& MONSTERS" WRITTEN BY
ASPASIA PROTOGEROU AND
ILLUSTRATED BY ALECOS
PAPADATOS WAS PRINTED ON
ONE HUNDRED AND FIFTEEN GSM
GARDAMATT ART PAPER AND
BOUND BY "M-S PRESS S.A." IN
MARCH 2016 ON BEHALF OF
POLARIS PUBLISHERS